BRITISH SEA BIRDS

The endpapers to this book portray flying Gannets. The first of these is a very young bird and the last is a second summer bird.

TO

MARGARET AND BRUCE CAMPBELL

PORTRAIT OF A PUFFIN. [*Frontispiece*

BRITISH SEA BIRDS

WRITTEN & ILLUSTRATED

by

C. A. GIBSON-HILL
M.A., M.B.O.U.

with photographs by the author

H. F. & G. WITHERBY LTD.
5 WARWICK COURT, LONDON, W.C.1

First published 1947

PRINTED IN GREAT BRITAIN BY
NORTHUMBERLAND PRESS LIMITED
GATESHEAD ON TYNE

THIS book gives short biographies, singly or in groups, of the twenty-four sea birds breeding regularly in the British Isles. At the end is a summary of their chief field characters and nesting distribution, together with brief notes on the identification of the majority of the additional species occurring as migrants or occasional strays. The biographies are illustrated with photographs, taken specially for this work, of all except the petrels which, like the Manx Shearwater, are not seen on land in daylight. The order and Latin names follow the current issue of the *Handbook of British Birds* for the convenience of readers, though I am not satisfied that in all cases the latter are the most suitable.

In seventeen species the nesting distribution is illustrated by small maps. These have been drawn to give a general impression of the range, rather than precise data for individual localities. In several instances records of occasional breeding by a few pairs have been omitted intentionally. Every attempt has been made to keep the maps as accurate as possible, but recent information is not available for all parts, particularly north-west Scotland and Ireland. Several species are at the moment expanding and others have an unfortunate habit of changing their nesting grounds. Some have vacated recently colonized sites as a result of the coastal activities during the war years, while others seem to have moved, possibly temporarily, into areas from which the public was excluded. In covering Ireland I have been much assisted by various correspondents, especially J. A. S. Stendall of Belfast Museum in the case of Ulster. I am also much indebted to P. A. D. Hollom, who read the first draft of the book and suggested a number of important modifications.

The photographs were taken in the summer of 1946, such as it was, mostly on the sites marked on the accompanying map. In making the necessary visits I was assisted greatly by the kindness

and co-operation of many people. A full list would be very lengthy, but even in this short space I would like to acknowledge my indebtedness to R. M. Lockley and John Buxton (Skomer and Grassholm), H. C. Jones (Puffin Island), A. and J. Girvan (Ailsa Craig), Samuel Bruce, G. T. Kay and Dr. G. MacInnes (the Shetlands in general), Richard Perry and George Sutherland (Noss), Lawrence Bruce (Herma Ness), L. S. V. Venables (Flotta), George Waterston and Frank Elder (Isle of May) and, in determining the correct people to contact, Bruce Campbell and James Fisher. All these men are ornithologists, or friends of ornithology, and freely gave all the help that lay in their power.

C. A. GIBSON-HILL.

Contents

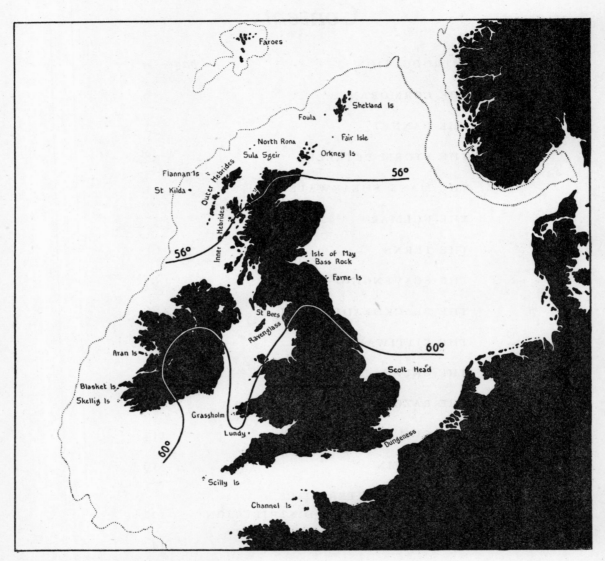

Sketch map showing the British Isles and adjacent portions of the Continent. The Faroe Islands formerly belonged to Denmark but are now independent. The fine dotted line marks the hundred fathom level, the boundary of the continental shelf. The unbroken lines across the British Isles are the July isotherms for 56° and 60°; these have been repeated on some of the maps in the last section of the book.

Introduction

THE men and women of the British Isles take more interest in their birds, and have discovered more about them, than the inhabitants of any other country. Yet, in some respects, there is a certain monotony in most of the easily accessible kinds, except, one would suggest, among the sea birds. There are places in the world where one finds more sea birds and even, possibly, a greater range, but I know of nowhere where there is such richness and abundance within easy reach.

There is a fascination about sea birds that does not exist, to the same degree, in any other habitat group. It is the cumulative effect of the natural attraction of their surroundings and the extent to which they fit into them. The sea, and even more the sea edge,

> *. . . the bold anfractuous rocks*
> *Faced by the snarled and yelping seas,*

are places of movement, the waters restless and troubled, and the air seldom still. Much of the charm of birds is in their lively combination of form and movement. In sea birds this reaches perfection. They may look ungainly, even human, when at rest, they may fly or swim clumsily, but for each there is some action that it exercises as near to finality as would seem possible. The world can show few things as memorable as a penguin fishing in antarctic waters; a wandering albatross gliding through a South Atlantic gale; a frigate-bird idling on the simmering air above a coral lagoon; or petrels, fluttering like great-winged black butterflies, in the rolling troughs of a deep sea storm,

> *trembling black wings fingering the blowy air,*
> *dainty and ghostly, careless of the scattering salt.*

In our own off-shore waters there is the lovely, curving, banking flight of the shearwater; the great white wings of the gannet against a blue sky; and the little flurry and flick of its legs with which the guillemot dives.

By their name sea birds should be those that appertain to the sea, but of necessity the group is a loose one. Man, who sometimes tries to keep clear his thoughts, attempts by habit to pigeon-hole the world round him. In reality it has no hard lines and no sharp divisions. A few birds belong almost completely to the wide wastes of open water, though none living, like the Halcyon, lay their eggs on the ocean. A great number of sea birds spend most, or all, of their time on the borders of it. Here those that live on the edge of the sea often differ little in their habits from those on the outer edge of the land. There are no standards by which one can inevitably put a bird in one category or the other. In the end, however much one may invoke scientific canons, it is a question of feeling: some of the borderline birds have the taste of the sea about them and others, to the individual, do not.

Twenty-four birds are treated in this book, and for the purpose of it they are the sea birds breeding in the British Isles. Dr. R. C. Murphy, in his *Oceanic Birds of South America*, included phalaropes, oyster-catchers and certain of the southern ducks and geese. W. B. Alexander, in his invaluable *Birds of the Ocean*, omitted all of these except the phalaropes. In this book the process has gone further and even the phalaropes have been left out. In parts of the southern oceans one sometimes meets them far in the open sea during the summer months, swimming in little groups like miniature gulls, but on British coasts they are essentially marsh birds.

The families that might best have been included are the divers and eiders. All that I have granted them is two photographs: if I ever write a book on the birds of the coast I will try to make amends. They live almost entirely on the fringe of the sea, feeding largely, and in the case of the eiders solely, in salt water. The divers nest no farther from it than the Common Gull and nearer than most Blackheaded Gulls, while the Common Eider breeds only on coastal sites. But to me they have the feel of the shore rather than the sea. Possibly because I have not yet been to Spitzbergen I cannot conceive of them in a storm or plodding over a great wilderness of empty, restless water.

The Blackheaded Gull is even less of a sea bird, in itself, than the divers and eiders; many of its breeding-sites are far inland and during the early summer months it is rarely seen on the shore; but it has about it the magic of being a gull. Even at their best many of the gulls are no more than coastal creatures, but like the little coal brigs that crept from port to port when I first went to Cornwall, they come in from the sea with the tide and seem to be but on holiday from trafficking in great waters. Coastal they may be, but they evoke the images that T. S. Eliot crystallized,

> Gull against the wind, in the windy straits
> Of Belle Isle, or running on the Horn,
> White feathers in the snow, . . .

Certain of our breeding sea birds belong almost completely to the open ocean and only come ashore, and then with considerable reluctance, to lay their eggs. Outside the nesting season they disperse well away from land. The two storm petrels, the Kittiwake, and, to a lesser extent, the Fulmar, the two skuas and the Puffin, belong to this group. So do some of our casual, occasional visitors. Wilson's Petrel which nests in the Antarctic, the Sooty Shearwater from Cape Horn and the Great Shearwater from Tristan da Cunha, all spend their holidays on a great clockwise tour of the North Atlantic. During this period they are uninterested in, and even shun, land, but storms and contrary winds sometimes bring them on to our coasts. Certain of the other petrels and shearwaters that nest on Madeira, the Canaries, the Cape

Verde Islands and even the West Indies and drift out into the mid-Atlantic away from their breeding seasons, occasionally arrive the same way.

Some of our breeding sea birds belong typically to the off-shore zone or outer coastal waters. Like the others they leave the land for the open sea during the winter months, but travel less far from it and are more likely to be driven back by bad weather. The Gannet, the Manx Shearwater, the Razorbill and the two guillemots belong to this group. Sometimes, when food is plentiful near the shore, they may remain at no great distance away for part or all of the winter. This applies particularly to the Gannet. In 1945 a mild and rich autumn kept a number of these birds near the Shetlands. When more severe conditions set in early the following year they found food very scarce, and in February over five hundred sought shelter in Bressay Sound and Lerwick harbour. The Little Auk, which breeds north of the Arctic Circle, normally spends the winter months in coastal waters south to Norway, the Faroes, Iceland and Newfoundland, but it may travel farther, and prolonged bad weather occasionally drives it on to British coasts.

Bad weather is worse for a sea bird in coastal waters than for one out in the open, well away from land. The bird is in much the same position as the small boat sailor in a sound vessel. Given sufficient sea room it can ride out the wind, even if it is carried back several hundred miles in doing so. The bird's great problem is food. The plankton and small fish on which it normally feeds drop down from the surface in very rough weather, and so long as the storm lasts it may have to go hungry. In open water this is less important as it can reduce its expenditure of energy. Some species may even alight on the surface, though captive albatrosses are said to become sea-sick when the boat rolls badly. If, however, the bird finds itself drifting on to a lee shore the instinct to keep away from the land forces it to fight against the wind. The length of time for which it can do so cannot exceed the extent of its food reserves. After prolonged storms, particularly the autumn and spring gales, great numbers of off-shore birds are sometimes found dead or dying on parts of the coast; yet the smallest petrels can live through far worse weather in mid-ocean.

The remainder of our sea birds are essentially coastal or inshore birds. Two of these, the Common Cormorant and the Shag, are largely sedentary. A few individuals of the former appear to migrate, but the majority remain in the neighbourhood of their nesting-sites or disperse in home waters. The British terns are typically coastal birds, but they move to a warmer climate for the winter months. Some travel to Spain and North Africa, and others to South Africa and the Antarctic. The gulls, excluding the maritime Kittiwake, are also largely coastal birds, but they are less consistent as a group. The Common and Herring Gulls mostly disperse in home waters, like the cormorants. They are also joined by winter visitors from the northern parts of Europe: most of the Common Gulls on the east coast of England, where they are numerous during the colder months, come from Scandinavia and the Baltic. A

11

certain proportion of individuals of both species move inland, roosting on reservoirs and lakes. Here and on the shore they are joined by the Blackheaded Gulls. Great numbers of the two Blackbacked Gulls migrate to the Bay of Biscay and the Spanish coasts, while some individuals of the smaller species continue down the north-west coast of Africa, as far as Senegal; the remainder disperse with the Herring Gulls. A few, if fish are plentiful, move farther out to sea and spend much of their time in off-shore waters. With them, especially in the north, may be a varying number of Glaucous, and occasionally Iceland, Gulls, depending on the severity of the weather. For coastal birds the problem of the winter is largely one of food. If they can fish or scavenge they can manage. Severe storms are less menacing to them as they have no natural reluctance to taking shelter on the land.

There are always sea birds on our coasts and in the waters beyond them. The total of these movements means, however, that the population in autumn and winter is very different from that in the summer months. In autumn and winter the majority of the birds are scavenging gulls, and there are probably more of them, all together, than during the summer. With them are the Common Cormorants and, on the more rocky coasts, Shags, wherever fresh fish can be taken. In the off-shore waters there are Razorbills, Guillemots and Gannets, some Lesser Blackbacked Gulls and occasional Herring and Great Blackbacked Gulls. Farther out still, west into the Atlantic, are the Great Skuas, Kittiwakes, Fulmars and some of the petrels. South-west, still in open water, are Puffins, skuas and petrels. South in the off-shore waters of the Bay of Biscay are the Manx Shearwaters and more Gannets, many of them younger birds. Along the coast of the Continent are the migrated gulls and the Little Terns.

At various times in winter and spring these birds come back to our coasts. The earliest arrivals are the first Fulmars, who may reach their nesting-sites as soon as November or December. After them come the Razorbills and Common Guillemots, who begin to move into the neighbourhood of their breeding-grounds in January, though they seldom take up permanent residence on the land before April. The Gannets and Manx Shearwaters start to arrive in February or early March, and the Puffins at the end of the latter month. After them, in March and April, come the gulls and, in April and May, the skuas and terns and the Storm Petrel. By then the whole picture has changed. In the more thickly populated parts gulls are still the most conspicuous birds, but away from man, on the sandy shores and steep cliffs, they are completely dwarfed by the great numbers of terns and auks.

The Herring and Blackbacked Gulls nest all round our coasts and, except in the extreme north and between Yorkshire and the Isle of Wight, the Common Cormorant is fairly widely distributed. For the rest the birds group themselves according to the nature of the coastline and the degree of isolation. The terns occur mostly where there are sandy or shingle beaches, or low rocky islands. The Shags, Kittiwakes,

Razorbills and Common Guillemots are restricted largely to areas of steep cliffs, and the Gannets to a few precipitous stacks. The Manx Shearwater, the Storm Petrel and most of the Puffins congregate on larger, turf-covered, fairly isolated islands.

Sea birds are defenceless at their nesting-places, and most of them can do little against the attacks of rats, stoats and men. Those, like the Kittiwake and the Common Guillemot, breeding on almost sheer cliffs are fairly immune from attack. Many of the remainder now concentrate on stacks or islands where they are seldom molested. When, as seems to have happened on Lundy, rats are introduced, their numbers decrease steadily. The British Isles are not alone in this. Certain of the mid-ocean islands, such as some of those in the Tristan da Cunha group, have lost their sea birds with the arrival of the ubiquitous rodent, while on others they have been seriously reduced by wanton destruction and excessive slaughter for food.

The British Isles are spread over eleven degrees of latitude, and the summer temperatures in the south are normally appreciably warmer than those in the north. Certain of our sea birds appear to be well adapted to the full range and the distribution of their breeding grounds is largely dependent on the occurrence of suitable sites. In others, climatic conditions seem to be a limiting factor. The largest colony of Gannets is on St. Kilda, but the steady increase in numbers on Grassholm and the recent spread to the Channel Islands suggest that it flourishes at least as well in the south. The Common Cormorant and the Shag are also fairly evenly distributed, though the former is relatively less numerous in Scotland and the latter in England, but the greater concentration of isolated cliffs in the north is probably at least as important as the climate. The same point would seem to apply to the Razorbill, Common Guillemot and Kittiwake. Suitable nesting-sites is certainly the dominant factor in the distribution of the Manx Shearwater, the Storm Petrel and the Puffin, and the widely spread Herring and Blackbacked Gulls.

Many of the remaining birds appear, to some extent, to be effected by climatic conditions. The Little Tern is scarce in the highland zone of Scotland and does not occur on the mainland in the north, while the Roseate Tern reaches its most northerly point in Fife. The Common and Sandwich Tern penetrate as far as the Orkneys, but are much less plentiful than the Arctic Tern throughout north-west Scotland. On the other hand the Common Gull and the Black Guillemot only breed at a few scattered points in England, and reach their greatest concentration in the north-west of Scotland and the Northern Isles. Since 1878 the Fulmar has spread over the greater part of the coast of Scotland and Ireland, and has established breeding pairs as far south as Cornwall, but it is still predominently a northern bird; but in spite of its colonization about ninety per cent of the Fulmars breeding in Britain are on St. Kilda, the Outer Hebrides, Orkneys and Shetlands. The Arctic Tern occurs as far south as the Scillies, but it again is most plentiful in the north, and in the Shetlands is the only tern usually seen. The Arctic Skua reaches as far south as Caithness and Sutherland: the Great Skua only as far as Hoy in the Orkneys.

The majority of the British sea birds nest in colonies, often of considerable size. Sometimes, as in the Kittiwakes on Grassholm, these appear to remain fairly static over long periods. In other species they sometimes increase or decrease rapidly, often for no apparent reason, while a few have a habit of abandoning sites after a number of years and moving to a fresh one near by. The Sandwich Tern is particularly notorious in this respect. Sometimes its increases are as marked as its withdrawals. For years it bred sporadically on the Isle of May and in 1945 there were about fifty pairs: the following year there were over five hundred. The Puffin also moves about and there are a number of abandoned colonies on different islands. About 1890 there were said to be over a quarter of a million pairs on the uninhabited island of Grassholm: in 1933 R. M. Lockley could find only about a hundred birds. In the same period the population of Skokholm, seven miles away, rose from two small colonies to approximately 20,000 pairs, giving an average density of 86 pairs to the acre. In the same way in the middle of the last century the Gannets abandoned Lundy, where they had been breeding since at least as far back as 1274, and appear in part to have moved to Grassholm.

The urge to nest in company is marked in most sea birds, and is by no means always due to a shortage of suitable sites. All the British species, except perhaps the Black Guillemot, show it to a varying degree, and in some it is very strong. Sandwich Terns will concentrate as thickly as nine nests to the square metre, even when there is plenty of space available for expansion on the outskirts of the colony. Roseate, Common and Arctic Terns even mix in with each other, to form a compact mass. Herring and Lesser Blackbacked Gulls sometimes form adjacent colonies and at others, when there is few of one species, join together. Gannets, Skuas, Shearwaters, Puffins, Common Guillemots, Razorbills and Kittiwakes all prefer to nest as close as possible to members of their own kind or even, in the case of the last three, merely to each other rather than as isolated pairs. Gannets, Kittiwakes and Common Guillemots will pack closely in most unfavourable places, leaving broader ledges a hundred yards or so away untenanted. Skuas, Terns and Blackheaded Gulls get very excited, in their different ways, if another bird approaches too close to their nest and are constantly being provoked by their neighbours, but they seldom withdraw to a splendid isolation where they could breed undisturbed.

An interesting feature of this extreme sociability is the extent to which individual birds are influenced by their neighbours. In certain species, the scavenging gulls, the Common Cormorant, Leach's Forktailed Petrel, the Razorbill and, peculiarly, the Black Guillemot, who seems to court in company and nest in solitude, the initial stages, at least, of the display are communal, just as they are in the Wandering Albatross and some of the waders. Even apart from this the erotic impulses of a pair appear to be heightened by the activities of others round them. Cormorants, Gannets, Fulmars and gulls all breed more successfully when in large colonies than when they nest as scattered pairs, in spite of the fact that the latter birds will steal each other's eggs and young whenever they have a chance to do so. The same principle appears to apply among the Common Terns in the New England states where the chick yield has been shown to be appreciably higher in the larger colonies. In Britain there would seem to be a threshold number of pairs in the case of the Razorbill and Fulmar, and possibly the Common Cormorant and Gannet, at least, below which breeding is unlikely to occur. This means, of course, that distribution may be limited not by the absence of sites on which one or two pairs might breed, but by the absence of ledges large enough for a sufficient number of pairs to be close together. It would also account for the difficulty that some of these birds appear to have in beginning a new colony, and the way in which colonies suddenly disappear.

Dr. A. O. Gross, working in America, has shown that Herring Gulls frequently return to their respective natal colonies to breed. Data collected on other species, including Kittiwakes in Greenland, Common Terns in Massachusetts, Manx Shearwaters in Wales and Southern Cormorants in Holland, lead to the same conclusion. It would seem to be the general rule among gregarious sea birds. This means that, as far as numbers are concerned, nothing succeeds like success. The larger colonies produce a higher proportion of chicks, and the more fledglings that are reared the more recruits the colony will have when they reach maturity. Once a colony has become well-established it should normally expand automatically until it has reached the limits of space and of the amount of food available, or highly successful predators arrive.

Another interesting aspect of this question is that of the age of the breeding birds. Birds do not invariably return to the same spot year after year, but prolonged, large-scale ringing, carried on since 1928, among the tern colonies off Cape Cod has shown that the tendency to do so increases with age, and that the older birds have a stabilizing effect on the colony as a whole. They begin the work of reproduction earlier and carry it through more steadily. The same conclusion has been reached by A. Kortlandt working on the Southern Cormorant in Holland, and would certainly seem to apply to the Gannet, Fulmar and Shearwater at least in Britain. Thus it would seem that a colony itself matures and becomes more efficient as it grows older as well as larger. However individual these birds may appear to be when one meets them scattered over the open sea, there is no doubt that together, on their nesting grounds, they are frequently a unit for reproducing that is more than the mathematical total of its component parts. There they are themselves but members of an individual, more important for the species than they are singly.

The Cormorants

THE cormorants are a widely distributed family of birds, comprising some thirty species. They occur in all parts of the world, except the central area of the Pacific, though they are most plentiful in temperate waters. They have slender, cylindrical bills with a sharp hook at the end, long necks and wedge-shaped tails. The wings are broad and fairly long. The feet are large and seem clumsy on land. Like the gannets they have all four toes united in a single web.

The cormorants are sociable birds and are usually found nesting, fishing or flying in small groups. They are essentially coastal dwellers and are not often met far from land. Once in the Antarctic a whaling skipper, seldom sober and a bad navigator, told me that he never worried about land until someone saw a group of cormorants: then he always set a watch for it.

Two species, the Common Cormorant, *Phalacrocorax c. carbo*, and the Shag (or Green Cormorant), *P. a. aristotelis*, nest in the British Isles. There are minor points of difference in their distribution and feeding habits, but they are frequently found breeding in the same locality and are, in general, very similar to each other.

The adults of both species are almost entirely dark in colour. The Common Cormorant, which is the larger with a wing span of over four feet, is a fairly uniform, glossy, bluish black, with the wing coverts and scapular feathers bronze-grey edged with black, and the chin and sides of the face white, or, in winter, brownish white. In the breeding season this bird develops a patch of white on the thighs and a few white feathers on the crown and back of its head. The bill is lead-grey on the maxilla and horn-yellow on the mandible, with the bare facial skin a light greyish yellow. The irides are bottle-green, and the feet and legs black.

The Shag is a slightly smaller and more graceful bird, with a span of about three and a half feet. It is similar in plumage, but lacks the white areas of the Common Cormorant, and has a rich greenish gloss in place of the latter's bluish sheen. The bill and feet are blackish, and much of the naked facial skin a full, rich yellow. The irides are sea-green.

Cormorants usually travel fairly close to the water with a steady, purposeful flight. They seldom cross over land, and when they do, generally rise high in the air. The neck is well stretched out. The regular flapping of the wings is broken only occasionally by short glides. Their flight is something like that of a duck, but it is less hurried and has an unpleasantly determined, business-like quality about it. One has only to see them, slowly winging their way home against the red glow of a fading sun, to realize why Milton gave Satan the shape of a cormorant.

Guillemots and Kittiwakes nesting on the
Pinnacle Rock in the Farne Islands.

Above : a Gannet alighting on the colony at Ailsa Craig
Below : Great Skuas bathing in a lochan on Herma Ness.

Above: a Red-throated Diver in the water.
Below: an Eider Duck on her nest.

Above, a Cormorant
feeding one of its
chicks, and below,
two young birds.

[20]

family

ommon
ormor-
ts
their
st on
ffin
and.

Green Cormorants on the Farne Islands, above, an adult with three downy chicks, and below, two parents with a fully fledged youngster (on the left). [22]

A Green
Cormorant
or Shag,
taken at
Herma
Ness in
The Shet-
lands.

[23]

The Gannet
Above: an adult with
a chick in full down.
Below: a ten-day old
chick with the down
just appearing.

Portrait of a Gannet taken on Herma Ness in the Shetlands.

The Gannet in the air, above, in normal gliding flight, and, below, with head and tail raised and feet lowered as it drops down to alight. [26]

The Gannet coming down to alight   The bird in the upper pictures is carrying a piece of nesting material.

Typical sections of three Gannet colonies   Above, Grassholm off the coast of
Wales : below left, on the Noup of Noss in the Shetlands and below right, on Ailsa Craig   [2

Thence up he flew, and in the Tree of Life,
The middle tree and highest there that grew,
Sat like a Cormorant.

Cormorants swim low in the water, with the tail almost awash, paddling with the legs alternately like a duck. The bill is pointed upwards at an angle of about forty degrees, and not held horizontally as it is by the grebes and often by the divers. They feed almost entirely on fresh fish, which they catch under the water. They dive from the surface, not from the air. In general they seem to submerge in suitable places on the chance that fish may be there, though they sometimes spot shoals when on the wing. The Common Cormorant usually sinks quietly out of sight with no preparatory movement. When empty, the Shag generally springs up slightly, with its wings closed, and plunges head first. When full it slips away, seal-like, in the manner of the Common Cormorant.

They swim under the water in a series of rapid jerks, using both paddle-like feet simultaneously. The wings are kept tightly against the body, except when turning or rising to the surface. In clear seas they seem to chase by sight, but as they can fish equally successfully in muddy, estuarine water, it would appear that, as with the Japanese, hearing is an important help. It is also suggested, from observations made on captive birds, that in part the fish are attracted towards the cormorant by flashes of light reflected from the feathers on the back of its head. If the food is small it is swallowed before the bird re-emerges. If it is large or troublesome it is brought to the surface, and I have several times seen Shags battling with lengthy conger-eels which they had caught but could not overcome.

The British cormorants usually dive in fairly shallow water, submerging several times in rapid succession and then resting for a long period. The Common Cormorant generally feeds on or close to the bottom, frequently in estuaries and harbours. It may even fish inland, and it will deplete artificial tanks and ornamental ponds if not molested. It appears to take a great number of flat-fish and other edible kinds, and will also eat prawns and shrimps. It very seldom catches sand-eels or sprats. The Shag, on the other hand, normally fishes in more open water and usually enters estuaries only in bad weather. Its staple diet appears to be the sand-eel, but it also takes sprats. In general it would seem to be a coarser feeder, with a wider range of species to its credit. Both birds occasionally catch such fish as dragonets, wrasses and gobies, while the Shag in particular frequently takes species with well-marked protective adaptations or powerful defence mechanisms. Cormorants are highly efficient feeders, and a Shag has been seen to bring up six medium-sized wrasses in seven dives.

According to J. M. Dewar the optimum depth in the Common Cormorant is less than four fathoms, and the period under water frequently twenty to thirty seconds or less. The optimum depth for the Shag appears to be less than three fathoms, but it generally stays under for longer and dives of seventy, eighty-five and a hundred

The Green Cormorant or Shag.
(approximately ⅙ life size)

The Common Cormorant.
(approximately ⅙ life size)

seconds have been recorded. In ten complete series timed by W. H. R. Lumsden and A. J. Haddow the dives ranged from five to a hundred seconds, with an average duration of forty seconds. The number of dives per series varied from seven to twenty-nine, with an average of fifteen; and the overall time from six to twenty-three minutes, with an average of just over thirteen minutes.

When coming up cormorants frequently look round cautiously, with only the head and neck exposed, before bringing the back above the surface. If disturbed they immediately submerge again. At the end of a series of dives they usually lower their shoulders several times to scoop water over the back. The covering feathers seem to be less effectively waterproofed than in most diving birds, and they seldom rest on the sea when not feeding. Instead they withdraw to suitable rocks and sandbanks. There they stand for long periods drying themselves in the air, with their wings out, half-extended, like the Hapsburg eagle.

The Common Cormorant usually nests in small colonies of a few pairs to a hundred or more, on rocky islands and cliff ledges. Occasionally, especially in Scotland and Ireland, it may breed on inland water, and even in trees. Sometimes nests occur singly, particularly, it seems to me, in Cornwall. As with many sea birds, breeding appears to be more successful in larger units than it is in small ones or with single pairs.

The nest is usually placed on broad, flat ledges or the tops of stacks or islets. It is a rather large, untidy structure of sticks and seaweed, with the occasional addition of odd rubbish picked from the sea. The eggs may be laid any time between the middle of February and the beginning of June : April and May are the commonest months. A normal clutch contains three or four, but larger numbers, up to six or seven, are not infrequent. The eggs are a regular, elongate oval in shape and about 2·55-2·75 inches long. The shell is a very light blue, but its colour is usually obscured by a white, chalky deposit. Both parents incubate and the eggs take about twenty-eight days to hatch.

The young chicks are naked, with the skin brownish black, but soon develop a covering of thick, dark-brown down. They are fed by regurgitation by both adults. They grow rapidly and appear to be fully fledged in about nine weeks. The first feathering is a dull, drab brown, paler, almost white, on the underparts. The Common Cormorant is fairly sedentary in its habits and, though some individuals migrate, most remain somewhere within home waters.

The breeding habits of the Shag are rather similar to those of the Cormorant, but it is almost exclusively marine and does not frequent fresh water. It also usually nests in smaller units. The typical sites, on narrow cliff ledges or in caves, rock crevices or deep under overhanging boulders, are different from those of the Common Cormorant. As a result, though both birds often inhabit the same stretches of coast, they are seldom found breeding together. Even when they do occur at the same point the colonies usually remain discrete. On the Farne Islands the Common Cormorant nests in some numbers on the flat tops of Little Harcar and the Megstone, while the Shags are on the broken cliff face of Staple Island. On Puffin Island, off Anglesey, the former occurs on the broad ledges on the south side and the latter on the narrower, more overhung shelves on the north. On the Calf of Eday, in the Orkneys, the two species are very close to each other, but the Common Cormorants are on the summit and the Shags mostly on the side of the rock, so that even here there is little overlapping of their areas.

The eggs are like those of the Common Cormorant but frequently less than 2·5 inches long. The clutches are usually smaller, three being the rule and larger numbers rare. They are laid at intervals of three days, generally between the end of March and the beginning of June.

The Shag is sedentary within fairly wide limits. Dispersal may take place in any direction (though it is usually southerly) during the autumn and winter months, but the majority remain at no great distance from their breeding-sites. There is no evidence of migration to or from the Continent.

Both species are fairly plentiful over our coasts, with the Common Cormorant relatively more numerous in parts of the south and the Shag in Scotland and the north. On the whole they seem to be holding their own and in some areas are definitely increasing in numbers, as closely related birds are doing in America and on the Continent. According to P. A. D. Hollom there were thirty pairs on the cliffs at Freshwater, in the Isle of Wight, in 1937, and a hundred and twenty to a hundred and fifty in 1946. Local development has driven them from some stretches, but I noticed on a recent visit that the combined activities of the army, navy and air force had not displaced them from Poole Harbour. Their worst enemies appear to be the longshore fishermen, with whom the Common Cormorant in particular is most unpopular. The men believe that it seriously depletes the stock in the neighbourhood of its breeding-places and in consequence frequently raid the nests. On one island that I visited, after two attempts to obtain permission, I found that local fishermen had landed during the previous week and destroyed all but four of the hundred and fifty nests. According to A. Kortlandt, working on the Southern Cormorant, *P. carbo sinensis*, in Holland, a mortality among the young of between fifty and sixty per cent is necessary before the following breeding season for the population to remain stable. Over half the deaths in Holland are attributed to human activities. It would seem that without the interference of man both races would increase rapidly, for a time at least.

In Britain the name Cormorant, which first occurs in literature in the works of Chaucer, is usually restricted to the Common Cormorant, and Shag used equally exclusively for the Green Cormorant. Elsewhere, in the English-speaking world, the terms are interchangeable, scientists using cormorant and sailors shag for all members of the family. Cormorant is derived from the Old French *cormoran* or *cormorande*, which is itself a corruption of the Medieval Latin *corvus marinus*, through modification by the Breton *morvran*. The latter, *mor*, sea, and *vran*, a cow, has the same meaning as the Latin word. The origin of Shag is less certain, but it is probably the common noun used in reference to the untidy, forward-jutting crest carried in the early months of the breeding season. In Scotland and the north both birds are called *scart* or *scarf*, with a colour or size epithet for difference.

The Gannet

THE Northern Gannet, *Sula bassana*, is a lovely bird, particularly as one meets it out in open waters, with its great expanse of black-tipped white wing seen against the soft blue of a summer sky and the deep blue of a summer sea. It is the largest, and in many ways most impressive, of the British sea birds. It is also among the best known, though relatively few people have an opportunity of visiting its nesting-sites. Its general interest inspired J. H. Gurney to publish a long monograph on it in 1913, while more recently its attractiveness kept James Fisher and H. G. Vevers working for several years on a detailed report on its status.

The Northern Gannet belongs to a small group of nine species, all about the size of a goose, with stout, conical bills, fairly short necks and long, pointed tails. The wings are long and finely shaped. Six of these birds occur in tropical waters, where they are usually known as Boobies. Between them they populate all the coasts and the majority of the islands. One, inhabiting the coast of Peru, is among the principal producers of guano and of considerable economic importance. Before the war the collectable excreta of a single individual was said to be worth five shillings a year.

The tropical gannets are fairly distinct from each other in colouring and, in some cases, in their breeding habits. One, the Red-footed Booby, habitually nests in trees and will abandon otherwise suitable, isolated islands if the trees disappear. The temperate gannets, on the other hand, are all very similar. It has sometimes been suggested that their true relationship would be better expressed by regarding them as races of one rather than as three separate species.

The gannet occurring in Britain is confined to the north Atlantic, breeding north of latitude forty-five degrees north and in winter straying down as far as the tropic of Cancer. One of the other species, the South African Gannet, nests only on a limited number of islands off Cape Colony, from Saldanha Bay in the west, to Algoa Bay in the east. The third species, the Australian Gannet, breeds on a few small islands in the Bass Strait, off Tasmania and off the north island of New Zealand. I have never seen the latter alive, but I once spent a week on a South African island with a large colony of gannets a hundred yards from the door of the cottage in which I was living. Their behaviour, in even the smallest details, was almost completely identical with that of the British bird.

The Northern Gannet has a wing span of nearly six feet. In the adult the general colour is white, rising to straw yellow on the neck and head, with the primaries a dark, blackish brown. Occasionally, as a survival from immaturity, breeding birds may have the central one or two pairs of tail feathers the same colour. The bill is a light

The Northern Gannet.
(⅔ life size)

bluish horn, the bare facial skin purplish black and the iris pale grey. The legs and feet are black with an attractive light bluish green line along the dorsal surface of the digits.

It is easy to identify in the air, with a highly characteristic form and movements. When travelling it has a strong, purposeful flight, built up of three or four powerful wing-beats followed by a prolonged, steady glide in which little height is lost. The birds usually fly low over the water in small groups of two to a dozen or more. Often they form long lines, strung out one behind the other. Seton Gordon claims that the number in a party is nearly always odd, but I cannot say that I have found this to be so.

When over their fishing-grounds or nesting-sites, they generally glide backwards and forwards, maintaining themselves with considerable mastery and, if there is sufficient wind, very few wing-beats. This is particularly the case in the vicinity of the breeding-places, where the air is usually thick, from dawn to sunset, with gliding birds. Frequently the movement would seem to be a form of recreation, but there is no doubt that, like many sea birds, a returning Gannet takes a long time to summon courage to alight. Time and again I have watched an individual planing for half an hour or more, gazing earnestly at the site each time that it passed, before ultimately coming down.

Alighting is often an elaborate and acrobatic manœuvre. The bird first loses speed by dropping its legs, throwing up its head and increasing the inclination of its wings. Then, when just above the site, it bends its tail and head downwards, raises the tips of its wings and attempts to drop on the chosen spot. Generally it is successful. A bird that alights at the wrong point in a thickly packed colony is usually pecked and scolded on all sides until it blunders its way to the edge and gets into the air again. When settling on a cliff ledge the Gannet checks its speed by throwing the tips of its

34

wings forward in a beautiful deep curve, and then thrusts out its chest and feet to take the shock that still remains.

The normal diet of the Gannet is herring and other shoal fish. These are generally caught by diving from the air and subsequent pursuit under water. Occasionally Gannets will dive from the surface, like guillemots, or even pick up food like a duck or an albatross. They usually drop from a height of fifty to seventy feet, but it may be as much as a hundred or as little as five or ten. Sometimes swimming birds will jump into the air and plunge straight down from only a few feet.

The Gannet generally dives obliquely, falling rapidly with the wings half closed. As it enters the water they are folded completely, but even then the splash is considerable. When a number of birds are working over a large shoal of fish they seem to pour down out of the sky, "like so many projectiles". One can easily see the vividness of the Peruvian name of *El Piquero* (the lancer) for one of the tropical species.

Once it is under the surface the wings are half opened again, and the bird uses them to change its direction or assist it in elbowing its way through the water. The Gannet does not aim at a particular fish, but dives into the shoal and then searches for a victim amongst them. The food is usually swallowed before the bird emerges, but, as with the cormorants, large or troublesome items may be brought to the surface. Exaggerated estimates have been made of the depth of the Gannet's dive, but it is unlikely to exceed twenty-five fathoms and in most cases it is probably less than as many feet.

Normally the Gannet takes only fresh fish, but hungry birds, or youngsters, will sometimes join gulls in grubbing offal from the surface, and they will at times dive readily for flesh thrown into the water. In captivity, like penguins, they soon acquire the habit of eating dead fish handed out to them. The Gannet is essentially a sea bird, but it is occasionally seen over inland water in Scotland and has once been recorded fishing in fresh water.

The Gannet nests in compact colonies on small coastal islands. Typically the birds build on the narrow ledges of steep cliffs, but where they are not molested they may overflow on to the top of the island. It is essentially gregarious in its breeding habits and rather particular in its choice of site. As a result the number of recorded colonies is small, while some of them have very large populations. At present there are fourteen in Britain and a further nine spread over the Faroes, Iceland, Newfoundland and Canada. England has only one colony, small and struggling, at Bempton in Yorkshire, Wales has one with about 5,500 nests on Grassholm off Pembrokeshire, Ireland three and the Channel Islands one. The remainder of the British colonies are off the Scottish coasts, of which Ailsa Craig and the Bass Rock are the best known, and St. Kilda, with over 16,500 pairs, the largest.

The nest is an untidy structure, rather variable in size. It is usually composed of dried seaweed, but any local cliff plants or even shore refuse, from dead birds to golf balls, may be included. The birds generally begin to arrive at the British breeding-grounds in February or March, and nest building is usually well under way by April. The Gannet, like the penguin and other colonial breeders, is something of a thief and a good deal of material is filched from nest to nest. At the best the work is hap-hazard, with no real beginning and no end. Birds may bring back anything that attracts them all through the season: I took a long series of photographs of Gannets carrying nesting material at Ailsa Craig at the end of July.

The courting display is mutual and somewhat varied. The two birds stand facing each other with their necks extended, wings half spread and tails bent down. In this posture they twist their heads from side to side, occasionally trumpeting loudly as they do so. At intervals they may bow to each other and then, if close enough, strike their bills together as though fencing. Sometimes the latter movement passes on to a few gestures of mutual preening. Frequently pairs that are standing quietly to-gether are stimulated into displaying by the actions of a nearby couple, and on such occasions single birds may display on their own.

The single egg is usually laid about the middle of May. It is a regular oval and about 3·1 inches long. The shell is white, but it soon becomes stained an irregular mud brown. Both birds incubate, sitting with their feet, one over the other, on top of the egg. It takes about forty-three to forty-five days to hatch. The young chick is lead-grey in colour and completely naked, but it soon grows a thick covering of long, white down.

The first feathers, on the wings and mantle, appear when it is about six weeks old. It is fully fledged by the end of its third month. At this stage it is a dark slaty-brown spotted with white above, and white, with brownish grey edging on the feathers, beneath. The bill and feet are a dark brownish black. The plumage whitens with wear and successive moults, the complete process taking four or five years.

The young Gannets are fed with regurgitated fish. The parent brings the food up into its gullet and the chick puts its bill and head in to meet it half-way. They leave the nest when they are eleven to thirteen weeks old and make their way to the sea alone, gliding steeply from the cliff edge. The parents may remain on the empty site for some time, unmoved by the fact that, contrary to the usual practice, it is they and not the chick that have been deserted.

Gannets generally move away from their breeding-grounds in September, but if food is plentiful the adults may not go far. Normally they seem to spread south and west from Britain, as far as the Spanish coast and the Azores, but some have been recovered from northern Norwegian waters. A certain number enter the Mediter-ranean, and the Gannet is a fairly common winter visitor as far east as the coast of Palestine, though it does not reach north to Cyprus and Syria. The first-year birds usually move much farther than the adults; many of them appear to winter off the north-west coast of Africa, from Casablanca to Senegal. Extensive colour ringing might well show that the birds become progressively more nearly sedentary as they grow older, throughout their life, and possibly that, as with the Common Terns in North America, the older birds are the first to begin breeding each season.

At one time the Gannet was an important article of food and certain of the colonies were raided at regular intervals. This has largely ceased, and the only British colony still attacked is that on Sula Sgeir in the Hebrides. During the middle half of the nineteenth century the Gannet decreased in numbers as a result of both legitimate and wanton slaughter, but in the last sixty years it has more than recovered and is now increasing steadily. According to Fisher and Vevers the world population in 1939 was approximately 167,000 birds, of which about 109,000 were breeding in the British Isles. During the recent war at least two British colonies, Grassholm and the Scar Rocks, were used for bombing practice, but the damage does not seem to have been serious. In this period the Gannet extended its range and established a thriving colony on the Rock of Ortac and Les Etacs, off the west coast of Alderney.

The Gannet has two popular names. Gannet itself is from the Anglo-Saxon *ganot*, cognate with the Old High German *ganazzo* and the Latin *ganta*, a goose. Its alternative title, Solan or Solan Goose, is from *sula*, its Old Norse name. The terminal *-n* is from the suffix "the", which, as in the Icelandic *-hin*, follows the word that it qualifies. Formerly it had a number of names in Gaelic, of which the most attractive was *ian ban an sgadan*, the white bird of the herring. In France it is called *le fou de bassan*, the bird of the Bass Rock, and in Spanish *alcatraz*, from confusion with the pelican.

The Storm Petrels

THE storm petrels, of which there are twenty-two species, are among the smallest and most truly marine of all sea birds, with a size corresponding to that of the thrushes and swifts. Nearly all nest on small and relatively isolated islands. Outside the breeding season they scatter widely over the open sea.

They are quiet, secretive, gentle little birds, entirely nocturnal in their movements over the land. Some are very numerous, but one would never realize it from a visit to their nesting-places. One, Wilson's Petrel of the Antarctic, is probably the most abundant bird in the world. I have seen them as thick in the air as falling snowflakes over the whaling-grounds, yet few breeding-sites are known and at none do they seem to be particularly plentiful.

Two species, the Storm Petrel, *Hydrobates pelagicus*, and Leach's Fork-tailed Petrel, *Oceanodroma l. leucorrhoa*, nest in the British Isles. They are very similar in general appearance and for some time were not distinguished from each other. Both are a dark sooty-brown, with a white area at the base of the tail, the bill and feet black, and the irides dark brown. The Storm Petrel is the smaller of the two, with relatively shorter wings, a square-cut tail and an irregular whitish patch on the middle of the under surface of the wings. Leach's Petrel has rather longer wings, a browner colouring, a markedly forked tail, and the white area on the rump broad at the sides but almost interrupted in the mid-line.

Their flight has the distinctive characteristics of their family. They move close to the water, fluttering over an erratic, wandering course, rather like large-winged butterflies or small bats. At intervals they twist up into the air, are blown away like falling leaves in an autumn storm, and then swoop down to the water again, as though they were swifts hawking for insects. When feeding, or in very calm weather, they keep even closer to the sea and at such times often help themselves along by patting the surface with one or both feet. Occasionally they use the feet alternatively and give the appearance of walking on the water.

Their normal food is plankton, which they pick up from the sea as they flutter over it. They will also take any small fragments of oily refuse thrown from a ship. For this reason, and possibly because the propeller itself churns up quantities of their natural food, they frequently follow boats in open water. In strong seas, too, they collect round a vessel to feed in the strip of calmer water behind it, so that their presence in large numbers often presages a coming storm.

In very bad weather, and occasionally at other times, storm petrels settle on the sea. They float buoyantly, rather like corks, rising sweetly with the waves and gliding

The Storm Petrel
(life size)

Leach's Forktailed Petrel
(life size)

lightly down again in the trough behind them. Of the two species, Leach's Petrel takes to the water much more frequently than the Storm Petrel. It also has a wilder, freer flight, whirling away with the wind and then skimming down to the water like a shearwater, more often than its fellow. Frequently it can be distinguished on these points, even when it does not come near enough for the details of its shape and colouring to be seen clearly.

The Storm Petrel breeds in scattered colonies, of varying size, on a number of small islands off our coasts. No real nest is built, and usually only one egg is laid. It is a blunt oval in shape, dull white in colour and about 1·1 inches long. It is well hidden away, either at the end of an earthy burrow excavated by the birds themselves or, more frequently, in a natural crevice among loose stones. On Skomer I saw them breeding in old stone walls and, at one point, in the debris of a ruined building. According to R. M. Lockley the latter is by no means an unusual site, and he described to me an abandoned house in the Channel Islands where he found evidence of over a dozen pairs under the rafters of the roof.

This species nests later than most of our birds. In the south the first arrivals usually come in from the sea at the end of April or early in May, but the majority do not reach the breeding-grounds until towards the end of the latter month. In Scotland and the north they are several weeks later. The birds generally occupy the prospective site for two to three weeks before the egg is laid. At this period both parents may be together and, though mostly silent by day, they frequently croon softly to each other at night, emitting a prolonged, low churring note. This call is produced throughout the breeding season and has been heard as late as September. Individuals flying in from the sea sometimes call to their mates but, though the volume of sound is loud for so small a bird, they make much less noise than the nesting Shearwaters.

After the egg has been deposited only one bird remains on the nest. Both parents incubate, in spells of two to three days, while the other partner is away at sea feeding. The changeover always takes place at night and they are never seen near their nesting-sites by day. The egg takes about thirty-eight days to hatch.

The young fledgling, like those of all the petrels, has two coats of down. The first, soft and long, is a greyish, sooty-brown, paler on the ventral surface. The second, which succeeds its predecessor by continuous growth, is slightly darker. The chick is fed by both parents by regurgitation. Their arrival seems to be somewhat irregular and it may be left without food for two or three days at a time. The chick is normally silent, but it may greet its parents with a plaintive *teep-teep*, a note common to many young petrels. When, according to Lockley, it is about sixty days old they desert it and go back to the open sea. After a further seven to ten days it makes its way to the cliff edge by night and follows them. A ten-week-old chick that is put in the water by day immediately swims freely. It usually drinks as soon as it is in a position of comparative safety, and it may well be that thirst is normally the stimulus that forces it to move to the sea on its own.

The adults usually begin to disperse over the open water in the neighbourhood of their nesting-sites in August and September. Once they have ceased to visit the burrows they pay no further attention to the land until the following breeding season. In October they move farther out to sea, and by November they are well spread over the eastern portion of the North Atlantic, passing later to the regions south of the equator as far as forty degrees south latitude. Recoveries of ringed birds show that many return to the same nesting-places annually, at least up to four successive years, and it would seem that this is the normal procedure. Recent observations in America show Leach's Petrels breeding in the same burrows six and seven years after they were first ringed there.

Leach's Petrel is even more elusive than the Storm Petrel, and within our waters breeds on only four very isolated islands. So far I have not been able to visit any of them and, though still hoping to find someone to take me, have only seen this bird at sea. Accounts of it have been published by Dr. W. O. Gross in America, and J. A. Ainslie and R. Atkinson in Britain. From these it would seem, in general, to be similar, though earlier, in its breeding habits to the Storm Petrel. The egg, as might be expected, is rather larger, with a length of about 1·3 inches. An interesting feature of this species, which does not seem to occur to the same extent in the Storm Petrel, is the communal aerial courtship, during which the birds fly round in the dark over their breeding-grounds, calling loudly to each other.

The name petrel is usually considered to be a corruption of St. Peter, given to the birds from their apparent habit of walking on the water, but I am not satisfied that this is its origin. It, with the association, occurs first in an account published by Dampier in 1703. The earlier form, as in Flawes's *Voyage to Nova Zembla* (1676), was *pitteral*, which probably arose as a direct attempt to describe the pitter-patter of their feet. Their alternative name is Mother Carey's Chickens. Mother Carey is a corruption of *Mater cara* (beloved Mother), and probably comes from the opening words of the prayer which medieval mariners addressed to the Virgin Mary, when struck by storm or sudden disaster at sea.

The Manx Shearwater

THE Manx Shearwater, *Puffinus p. puffinus*, is the only British representative of a widespread family of attractive, medium-sized sea birds, closely related to the storm petrels. Like the latter they are nearly all strictly nocturnal in their movements at their nesting-sites, and outside the narrow limits of the breeding season disappear to the open sea. Little is known of the life cycle of many of them. Even the habits of the British member of the family were something of a mystery until R. M. Lockley began the observations on Skokholm, off the coast of Wales, which made him and his island famous among ornithologists.

The most interesting points of Lockley's work are those that go beyond a direct observation of the breeding cycle. He is acquiring a great deal of data on the speed with which nesting birds, taken and liberated at a distance, find their way back to their burrows. His most interesting case so far was a bird freed at Venice which returned to Skokholm in thirteen days: another, taken to Start Point, on the south coast of Devon, two hundred and twenty miles away by sea, was back in ten hours. Since all Manx Shearwaters appear much the same, some means of identification is necessary. This is achieved by placing a light aluminium ring, bearing a code number, on the bird's leg. The ring does not appear to inconvenience the bird, and, for the two to three years that it lasts, is as sure a label as a fingerprint.

The Manx Shearwater is about the size of a pigeon, with a wing span of thirty inches, the typical tubular bill and faint, musty odour of the petrels, and soft, appealing eyes. The upper surface is a rich, slightly brownish, black. The ventral surface, including the under side of the wings, is white, with the sides of the head and neck mottled with greyish brown. The bill is mostly black, shading to bluish grey at the base and sides of the mandible. The iris is black, and the legs and feet the cadaverous pink of a corpse, slightly bluish on the webs and marked with brownish black on the hind edge of the leg and the outer toe. When handled the bird has the demure, frightened appearance of a young rabbit, but, if too much worried, it fights effectively with both bill and feet.

The wings of the Manx Shearwater are long and narrow, with a rather lovely outline. It is the one of the many birds that I have never photographed in the air that I would most like to have taken. Its flight resembles that of the larger shearwaters. Its course is erratic, and it moves over the water in a long series of broad curves. Most of the time it glides with the wings rigid and fully spread. At intervals it gives a few quick beats, and then turns away on another long glide, swooping very low between the waves so that at moments, as it banks, the tip of its downturned wing seems to touch the water.

41

The Manx Shearwater.
(An adult from Skomer, Pembroke, ¾ life size)

The Shearwater does not follow boats, nor does it collect round them as the storm petrels do. In the open sea one usually meets it singly, or in small groups, so scattered that their appearance together seems to be due to coincidence rather than deliberate association. Even on their favourite fishing-grounds they remain a sparse mottling of isolated individuals.

The definite exception to this occurs in the neighbourhood of their breeding-places and the unmarked ocean roads leading to them. Here they collect, often in great numbers, and settle on the water waiting for the night to fall so that they can fly in to their nests. In the evenings one can see small flocks, steadily growing, winging their way purposefully and with an unusually direct flight, to the meeting-place. In the mornings, well away from them, one may see similar groups, not yet broken, setting their course for their feeding-grounds. Those from the Welsh islands go to the Bay of Biscay, and the parties frequently keep together at least until they have rounded Land's End.

Their food consists mostly of small fish, chiefly young sprats, herrings and pilchards, and small squids. It is generally picked from the sea as the bird hovers over the surface. Frequently they paddle with their feet while feeding, like the storm petrels. Sometimes they dive for it, using their wings under the water like a guillemot, but they never penetrate far and emerge after a very short interval.

The legs of the Manx Shearwater are stronger than those of the majority of petrels, but the bird nevertheless moves with difficulty on land. At the most it can walk upright for only a few paces. Its normal method of progression is with the tarsi bent. In this way it moves fast and with some facility on level ground. If it is hurried, or caught on an uneven surface, it usually scrambles along using its half-opened wings to claw it forward. When it comes upon serious obstacles it generally flutters up them, like a heavy-bodied moth.

It breeds on a number of fairly isolated islands round the west and north coasts of the British Isles and, in a few cases, on the mainland itself. Usually it forms large and thickly congested colonies. The single egg, which is a broad, blunt oval in shape, about sixty millimetres long and dull white in colour, is laid in a small, scantily lined chamber at the end of a burrow.

The burrows are generally two to four feet long. They are usually made in fairly soft, peaty earth, and are normally dug by the birds themselves. The earth is loosened with the bill, used rather like a pick, and then kicked out, terrier fashion, by the feet. Frequently they run very close to the surface and the ground over them is often too thin to support anyone walking over the colony. The work is always done at night, and the birds never venture outside their homes by day.

At Skomer the earliest Shearwaters appear off the island in February and the greater number have usually arrived by the end of March. At first they remain on the water, collecting and then dispersing again to feed, until the urge to reproduce overcomes their reluctance to leave the sea. Then they begin visiting the burrows, enlarging the old ones and digging new as needs dictate. Towards the end of the breeding season the bird's musty scent is imparted to the burrow, and an occupied site can sometimes be detected by its odour, though R. M. Lockley, wishing to produce a chick for a visiting photographer, once dug hard for some time and finally unearthed a young rabbit.

Once they are finally settled both birds frequently stay at home together, at intervals, until the egg is laid. Sometimes, according to Lockley, individuals are found in burrows other than their own. At the moment there is nothing to show whether this represents occasional promiscuity, or a genuine error on the part of birds that have not yet learnt to find their way unerringly to their own nests. Both parents incubate, in turns of two to three or more days, the absent partner disappearing south, sometimes as far as the Spanish coast, to feed. The egg takes about fifty-two days to hatch. For the first week or so one of the parents usually stays with the chick. After that it is only visited to be fed. When it is about sixty days old it is abandoned. By then it is almost fully fledged and heavier than its parents. For ten days or so it remains fasting. Then it makes its way to the sea and disappears like the adults.

All movement to and from the burrows takes place during the early hours of the night, from about two hours after sundown to between two and three in the morning. If there is much moonlight the land is shunned as if it were day, but in dull weather the air over the colonies is thick with flying birds. Courting couples, or those greeting each other, emit a prolonged, harsh churring note. Birds coming in from the water call loudly, producing a sound rather like a hoarse rooster being strangled, all too slowly, in the middle of his serenade. Although the Shearwater is normally silent at sea and by day, a large colony at night is a noisy and clamorous place.

The Shearwaters begin to leave their nesting-grounds in August, and all are away by the end of September or the middle of October. British waters appear to be deserted from November to January, but the destination of the majority is still uncertain. Initially they travel south to the Bay of Biscay, but there have been few mid-winter records from western France or northern Spain and it is possible that they move farther afield during the coldest months. Recoveries of ringed birds show that many return to the same nesting-place each year, and sometimes even to the same mates. A marked female bred on Skokholm for eleven successive years, while another pair occupied the same burrow for four years, deserting it only when one of the partners failed to turn up for the fifth season.

The Manx Shearwater has a number of enemies of which gulls, rats and men are the worst. The former pounce on any sluggards that the first rays of day find still over the land, and will even hunt for them on clear nights, by the light of the stars and a slipper moon, so that the ground round a colony is usually thickly scattered with dismembered corpses. Rats hunt them from their burrows and take the eggs and young. In the past men have been even more destructive, and at times thousands have been killed and ploughed into the ground as animal manure. As a result of these latter agents a number of colonies have been much reduced in size, or totally exterminated, in the last hundred years. Where, however, it is saved from these depredations the Shearwater flourishes, and, though there is nothing to suggest that the world total is increasing, on some islands it has grown more plentiful during the last thirty years. This is heartening, as even there only about fifty per cent of the pairs in a colony succeed in rearing a chick to the fledgling stage in a season, and reproduction does not begin until the birds are at least two years old.

Shearwater refers to the manner in which the bird skims close to the sea when in flight. Manx is now something of a misnomer, as the birds have not nested on the Isle of Man since 1800, but it was given to it at the time when that was the best known breeding-ground. The Latin name of *Puffinus* is also confusing. The Shearwater was first described by Brünnich in 1764, under the title of *Procellaria puffinus*, as the petrel that bred among Puffins in peaty burrows. Later, when it became reclassified as the type of a new genus, *puffinus* clung to it as its earliest scientific name. If the Manx Shearwater has any feelings in the matter it can at least console itself with the knowledge that the Turkey, a native of North America, is saddled with the vernacular name of a country in Asia, and the albatrosses with a corruption of the Spanish word for a pelican.

The Manx Shearwater.
Above : a bird at the entrance
to its nesting burrow on Skomer,
off the coast of Pembrokeshire.
Left and below, a bird having
a ring put on its leg for
identification.

[45]

The Fulmar, above,
launching into the
air from its nesting
ledge, and below,
two birds courting.

[46]

Nesting Fulmars, photographed in the Shetlands.

A Fulmar coming down to
alight at its nest.

[48]

A gliding Fulmar seen from above.
The white spots in the background are points of sunlight on the surface of the water.

Sandwich Terns nesting on the Isle of May, off the coast of Fife.

A Little Tern settling on its nest.

Above, an Arctic Tern, and below, a Common Tern In the former the outer tail feathers are usually relatively longer and the legs shorter than in the latter.

A Common Tern, above, alighting; and below,
carrying fish to its mate.

Roseate Terns
on the Isle
of May.
The birds in
the lower
photograph
are displaying.

[55]   Blackheaded Gulls nesting at Ystomllyn in Carnarvon.

A blackheaded Gull by its nest, and below, three newly hatched chicks.

The Fulmar

THE Fulmar, *Fulmarus g. glacialis*, is the largest of the British petrels, with a wing span of about three and a half feet and a weight of nearly two pounds. It has a heavy, tubular bill, a thick-set body, and a short, slightly pointed tail. Its wings are long and rather narrow, giving it, in flight, something of the appearance of a small, bulky albatross. Its eyes are large and gentle, with the patient, confiding look of a young fawn.

Its colouring is variable and three phases have been recorded. Most of the birds seen in the British Isles belong to the pale form, which is shown in the accompanying photographs. In it the head, neck and underparts are white, with a small, dusky area in front of the eye. The back, tail and dorsal surface of the wings are an uneven pearl grey, with the primaries darker. The bill is greyish or greenish yellow, marked with dark grey. The irides are dark brown, the legs and feet corpse coloured.

The dark phase, which is not known to breed east of Greenland, occurs occasionally in British waters as a stray visitor from the western Atlantic. It is ashy brown in colour, slightly paler on the underparts, with the same small dusky patch round the eye. The third form, which is often known as the Blue Fulmar, is distinctly paler. It may be almost white on the belly, but it is never so light as to be white on the head and breast. This phase breeds on some of the islands north of the British Isles. It is said to have nested on Fair Isle once or twice, but in general it occurs in British waters only as a non-breeding bird. I never saw any during an extensive tour of the Shetlands in June, in the course of which all the accessible colonies were inspected carefully.

The whiter birds bear some superficial resemblance to gulls, but the flight is very different. In the air the Fulmar, like the shearwaters, carries its wings rigidly and fully extended, without the marked angulation that characterizes the gull's. The normal flight, with a little wind to help it, consists of a series of long, gentle glides, with some wheeling and banking, broken by short intervals of slow, leisurely flapping. In calm weather the wing-beats are more frequent, but the Fulmar, like the albatrosses, generally drops out of the air when flying becomes too laborious.

In the neighbourhood of its breeding-sites the Fulmar, like the Gannet, spends much of the day planing backwards and forwards over the adjacent seas. At such times its mastery of the air is magnificent. Full value is extracted from every up-current and wing-beats are few. When playing in this manner the bird is idly inquisitive and will alter its course to pass once or twice near any new object on the cliff-top. Unfortunately its curiosity is usually short-lived, and after gazing quizzingly for a brief spell it quickly returns to its accustomed beat.

Much of this planing would seem to be mere recreation. No doubt, like many sea birds, it feels more at ease in the air than settled on a cliff ledge. At the same time it appears to have considerable difficulty in alighting. A sitting bird that has been frightened from its nest takes a long while to summon courage to settle back again. It will plane past the spot in a series of great ovals, edging nearer to the cliff each time that it goes by, for a quarter of an hour or more. Finally it may make as many as half a dozen feint landings before it feels sure enough of itself to leave the air.

The diet is rather varied and, though it is principally fish or fish refuse, Fulmars will take any oily matter that they find on the surface of the sea—even dead members of their own species. Their method of feeding is similar to that of the larger procellariiformes. Occasionally they swoop down and pick the food up as they pass over. Usually they alight on the water near by and swim cautiously towards it. Then, when near enough, they seize it hastily with quick, rather frightened, jabs of their bills. They float high on the water, with their heads held well up, "like high proud galleons", and paddle with their feet alternately.

The Fulmar's legs are too weak to support the weight of its body easily, and it rarely stands or walks. Its normal method of progression on land is to shuffle along, in an ungainly manner, with the whole length of its tarsi on the ground. In spite of this disability, and its apparent reluctance to alight, one frequently sees birds resting on cliff ledges, or even walls and buildings, in the neighbourhood of occupied breeding-places. They also visit new sites for several years before founding a fresh colony. During this period adults come ashore at intervals and squat on suitable ledges, so that a sitting Fulmar is by no means certain indication of the presence of an egg or chick.

The nesting-sites are very varied. Usually they overlook the sea, but birds have been found breeding as far as six, and in Spitzbergen twenty, miles inland. Typically they make use of fairly inaccessible cliff ledges, but, in the Shetlands where they are plentiful, one finds all manner of strange selections. Cliff-tops, buildings, walls or peat-stacks may be used in spite of the existence of empty, eminently suitable, ledges near by. Their choice seems to be as erratic and irrational as the war-time squatting of a government department.

Fulmars are not truly gregarious. At sea one usually meets them singly except when large numbers have been drawn to a particular spot by an abundance of food. At their breeding-sites they frequently collect in large colonies, but such units are much more diffuse than those of the Gannet or the Kittiwake. They have little inclination to pack in closely with their fellows. At the same time there is a great deal to suggest that the erotic activities of any one pair are greatly stimulated, as in the case of many sea birds, by the presence of others nesting near them. Every colony contains a number of non-breeding or unsuccessful birds, but the proportion of these sterile units is always much higher in a small group than in a large one.

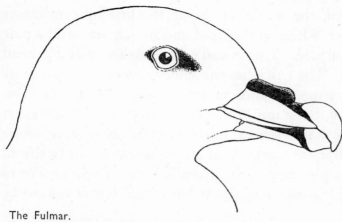

The Fulmar.
(An adult from Noss, Shetlands, ¾ life size)

The Fulmars may come in from the sea to visit their nesting positions as early as November. Usually most have arrived by the end of February, when they begin to take up a semi-permanent residence on the ledges. In general the birds arrive earlier in the older and larger colonies. It is doubtful if there is any true display, on the land at least, comparable to that of many sea birds. At the same time pairs show a considerable sheepish affection and may greet each other elaborately when they meet on the nesting ledge. The birds, facing each other or sitting side by side, raise their heads and sway them slowly up and down and from side to side, emitting a guttural bray as they do so. Occasionally they touch their bills together, and may actually seize each other. Sometimes these movements pass on to mutual nibbling of the feathers of the head and throat. An interesting feature of this period is the visits which non-breeding birds pay to those nesting on neighbouring sites, when the visitor and resident greet as though they were a mated pair.

Usually there is only one egg, which is not replaced if it is lost, but clutches of two occur occasionally. According to Professor Wynne Edwards Fulmars breed only once in every two or three years. The egg is normally laid at the end of May or the beginning of June. It is a pointed oval in shape, about three inches long and dull white in colour. Both sexes incubate, probably in spells of three to four days, and the egg takes about fifty-six to sixty days to hatch. If sitting birds are disturbed or frightened they vomit up an oily, yellow fluid and project it forwards with a range of about three feet. Since they are generally facing the intruder it might be regarded as aimed at him, but they are neither partial nor vindictive. The oil is thrown out when they are sufficiently provoked no matter what is in front of them at the time.

The origin of this fluid has not been established definitely. All that is known for certain is that it cannot be a direct product of digestion. The majority of the petrels behave similarly when disturbed, and in all cases where the substance has been examined it has been found to be almost identical. It also resembles closely the oil in the head cavity of the Sperm Whale and the preen gland of many birds. Its predominant constituent does not occur in the fish and plankton on which the petrels feed. The subject is at the moment being investigated by L. Harrison Matthews. In his opinion, as far as the work has gone, the fluid is probably formed as a waste product from the surplus oil in the bird's food, and excreted by the glands of the proventriculus.

The chick has two coats of down, the second replacing the first by continuous growth. In British birds the latter is white on the head and underparts, and a pale blue-grey on the wings and dorsal surface. The second coat is darker, with the head and neck included in the grey area. The chick has the same defence reactions as its parents. It is fed by both adults by regurgitation at intervals for about fifty days. Then they desert it and move away to sea until the end of the year. After a short time it follows them. Sometimes it makes several trial flights before leaving, while at others it seems to glide down to the water and then, after a short rest and a drink, make straight for the open sea. The plumage of the juvenile bird is fairly similar to that of the adult, and once the last fragments of down have been lost it cannot be distinguished in the field.

The Fulmar has few enemies apart from man, with whom it is not always popular. Fishermen, shepherds and crofters all have a certain dislike of it, though the exact cause of their emotion is not always clear. The worst that can be said of it is that it undoubtedly elbows other species away from its nesting-grounds. For some unknown reason no other bird will breed near it. In the past large numbers of Fulmars were taken for food, and even to plough into the ground as manure, but, though the young are still eaten in the Faroes, this practice has now stopped in Britain. The inhabitants of St. Kilda also used the oil as embrocation for rheumatism.

Until 1878, when it colonized Foula in the Shetlands, the only British breeding-place of the Fulmar was on St. Kilda. Since then it has multiplied rapidly, and has spread over most of the Scottish coast and the greater part of the Irish; in England it has reached as far as south Yorkshire in the east and in the west has established colonies in Cumberland, Wales, Devon and Cornwall. Birds have even been recorded prospecting on the coasts of Dorset and Normandy. The cause of this rapid spread, which was fully described in an admirable and detailed paper by Fisher and Waterston, published in the *Journal of Animal Ecology* in 1941, is not clear, but it is not, apparently, connected with the cessation of its use as food on St. Kilda.

Fulmar seems to be a corruption of the Old Norse *fúll már* (foul gull), given to it in reference to its musty odour. In the Shetlands it is usually called Mallie or Malli-mauk, which is the name that the Norwegian sailors in the Antarctic use for the smaller albatrosses. Its origin is obscure. Newton in his *Dictionary of Birds* derived it, through several corrupt forms, from the Dutch *mallemugge* (a small midge). He suggested that the vast collections of these birds round the dead whales reminded seventeenth-century Dutch whalers of the insects round a lamp, but the conception seems a little far-fetched.

The Terns

THE Terns, in general, are the most abundant and widespread of the popular groups of sea birds, and some forty-three species have been described. They are attractive, small to medium-sized birds, with long, tapering wings, fairly long, tapering bills, short legs and small feet. The majority, including all those normally occurring in Britain, have long, deeply forked tails. In contrast to their pleasing appearance their calls are usually harsh and raucous. Their typical habitat is the coastal areas of the warmer parts of the world, though some travel northwards in summer to breed in colder climates: one, the Arctic Tern, has been found nesting within eight degrees of the North Pole.

Five species, of which portraits in breeding plumage are given on a following page, nest regularly in the British Isles. Two of these here reach the limits of their range. One, the Roseate Tern, has its main breeding area to the south, while the other, the Arctic Tern, nests most abundantly north of sixty degrees north latitude. A sixth species, the Black Tern, *Chlidonias n. niger*, formerly bred in Britain. Unfortunately it has not done so since 1885, except for a few pairs which established themselves temporarily in Sussex during the early years of the war, on a marsh that had been flooded as a precaution against invasion. Similar action in Belgium in 1944 resulted in the Blackwinged Stilt and Pintail nesting there, and a great increase in the number of breeding Avocets.

The five terns still breeding here all belong to the same genus, and in many respects are very similar to each other. Their general colour is white, with the mantle and dorsal surface of the wings pearl-grey, and the primaries marked with dark slate-grey. In summer some have a faint rose-coloured blush, most obvious in the Roseate Tern, *Sterna d. dougallii*, on the feathers of the breast. During the same season all have the top of the head and the nape jet black, except the Little Tern, *S. a. albifrons*, whose forehead is white. In the Sandwich Tern, *S. s. sandvicensis*, the feathers of the crown and nape are elongated and form something of a crest. In this bird also they are sometimes moulted before the end of the breeding season, so that one may see individuals still about their nesting duties with patchy, mottled heads.

In the Sandwich Tern, which is larger than the others, the legs and feet are black, and the bill black with a yellow tip. In the Little Tern, which is appreciably smaller, the legs and feet are orange-yellow, and the bill yellow with a black tip. The remaining three species are very similar in size and appearance. The Common Tern, *S. h. hirundo*, with a wing span of about thirty inches, has the legs and feet red, and the bill coral-red with a black tip. The Arctic Tern, *S. macrura*, which in the field can only be distinguished from it with difficulty, usually has the legs, feet and bill a uniform blood-red. In the Roseate Tern the legs and feet are red, and the bill black, dropping to vermilion at its base. In winter plumage our terns have a varying amount of white on the forehead and crown, the bills darker or completely black, and the legs and feet duller or even greyish.

The nesting habits of some of these birds differ slightly, but in general their behaviour is very similar. They are typically coastal birds, seldom occurring far inland and, except on migration, seldom being found far out at sea. They are very sociable and frequently fly and feed in scattered groups.

They are light and buoyant in the air, and their flight is most attractive. The wing beats, each of which raises them perceptibly, are deliberate and rather slow. At intervals they break the sequence with short, swallow-like glides. The Little Tern flaps its wings more frequently than the others, and the Sandwich Tern is heavier, and more gull-like, in its flight, but all are extremely graceful. Their white wings and bodies against the rich blue of the sky are as much one of the joys of summer as the great white sails of the yachts in the Solent.

They feed mostly on small fish. Some will also eat crustacea and molluscs, and even insects, but they never scavenge like the gulls. The food is usually taken from the surface of the sea. When fishing they fly slowly over the water, at a height of ten to twenty feet, with the head turned down. Occasionally they swoop and pick the food from the water without entering it. Usually the bird drops with half-closed wings and, with surprisingly little splash, submerges its head and body. Sometimes, but less frequently, they disappear completely for a few seconds.

Terns seldom alight on the sea for long, though they are cleanly birds and much enjoy short bathes in the water. Usually they rest, often in small groups, on out-lying rocks and sandbanks or the shore itself. They also make use, as the cormorants do, of old jetties and the posts of breakwaters. One tropical species has even been recorded trying to alight on the head of a floating pelican rather than come down on the surface of the sea.

Terns are fairly noisy birds and they generally call to each other when fishing. They are inclined to be quarrelsome at their nesting-sites, and, even when they are not disturbed by intruders, the clamour is considerable. Each bird that alights is shrieked at by its neighbours, and usually shrieks in return. A peculiar and unexplained feature of this babel is the occurrence of sudden silences, following which all the birds rise in a cloud and fly round together as a compact flock. After one or two circuits the flight usually breaks up, and the birds return individually to their nests and there resume their bickering.

The terns are gregarious in their nesting habits and frequently form large colonies. Sometimes these contain two or more species, either mixed together or in adjacent blocks. In the north the Arctic Tern often nests close to the Common Gull, and in

The Little Tern.

The Roseate Tern.

The Arctic Tern.

The Common Tern.

The Sandwich Tern.

(all sketches approximately life size)

England the Sandwich Tern sometimes occurs in company with the Blackheaded Gull. An interesting, though troublesome, characteristic of some of these birds, particularly the Sandwich Tern, is the habit of selecting a site, building up a large colony over a number of years and then suddenly deserting it. The fact that terns have bred successfully in a particular spot for several seasons is no assurance that they will come back to it indefinitely.

In a normal season the terns arrive at their nesting-sites from early April to the middle of May in the south, and begin laying two to three weeks later. The date varies to some extent with the species. The Sandwich Terns are usually the first to arrive, followed by the Little and Common Terns. The courtship, which has been well described by G. and A. Marples in the case of the Common Tern, is an elaborate and attractive performance. During the course of it the two birds catch and feed fish to each other in turns. When displaying on the ground they frequently raise their tails, droop their wings and bow to one another. The moves and responses are very similar in all the British terns, particularly among the three medium-sized species. In a mixed colony individuals may display successfully to representatives of another species, and cases have been recorded of Common and Roseate terns breeding together. The male tern, like man and Fabre's weevils, is an amorous, unsatisfied creature and may demand coition all through the breeding season.

The Little Tern usually breeds in fairly small, scattered colonies on sand or shingle banks near the sea. The eggs, which may be two or three in number, are placed in a shallow, unlined depression made by the female bird. The Sandwich Tern has a much wider range of sites, and may nest on shores, sand-dunes or low-lying, rocky islands. It generally lays one or two eggs and the nesting-hollow is often lined with a few wisps of grass or pieces of stick. It frequently assembles in larger, more compact groups than the Little Tern. On the Isle of May I saw a colony of over five hundred pairs, with a maximum concentration of nine clutches to the square metre.

The Common Tern has about the same range of sites as the Sandwich Tern, but may nest farther from the sea and often occurs in very large colonies. The normal clutch is three. The Arctic Tern frequently chooses similar sites to the Common Tern and may mingle with it. In the Shetlands I have seen colonies on bare patches of shingle on an open moorland nearly a mile from the coast. The normal clutch is two, but three eggs are not uncommon. The Roseate Tern generally breeds on small rocky islands in company with other terns. The eggs, normally one or two in number, are usually placed in a hollow among rocks, or close to a stone outcrop. These three birds will all add a little nest lining if there are any suitable sticks or bits of grass near, and be quite content without if there are none.

Most terns show considerable individual variation in the colouring of their eggs. They may be whitish, pale greenish olive, grey or buff in ground colour, and mottled, streaked or scrawled with grey, black or brown of varying shades. They may even be unmarked. Greenish or greyish tints seldom occur in those of the Little Tern (about 1·3 inches long) and the Sandwich Tern (about 2·1 inches long). The eggs of the other three species may show any of the possible colours.

The eggs are normally laid, at intervals of two days, towards the end of May or early in June. Incubation begins with the appearance of the first egg and both birds brood, though the female usually does the greater part of the work. Frequently the male brings her offerings of fish while she is on the nest. Incubation takes about three weeks. Terns rise easily from their nests but are very aggressive in their defence. Once in the air they wheel round, shrieking harshly, and swoop at, and in some species attempt to strike, the intruder.

The newly hatched chicks are covered with a thick down, yellowish or greyish in colour with darker markings. For the first two or three days they stay in the nesting depression, brooded by the female, while the male brings food. Later both parents feed them and the youngsters may stray a little, particularly if disturbed. Young Sandwich Terns are usually taken down to the shore near the colony, where they assemble in small groups, when they are ten to fifteen days old. Here they are fed communally, like the chicks of the Gentoo Penguins, a returning adult making no attempt to find its own but surrendering its food to the nearest or most clamorous youngster. The smaller terns are fully fledged in about four weeks, the Sandwich Tern in five. At this stage they can fly, and will readily take to the water and swim freely. They are generally fed for a further week or ten days, and then left largely to fend for themselves. The juvenile plumage resembles the adult winter plumage except that the feathers of the back, and sometimes the crown and wing coverts, are mottled with brown or grey.

Some interesting observations have been published recently on the Common Terns breeding off Cape Cod, in southern Massachusetts. From large-scale ringing operations, carried on since 1928, it would appear that the average life span is about ten years, with a small but recognizable number living to eleven or twelve years. About one in two hundred were found to survive for a longer period, of which five were recorded as far as their eighteenth year. The majority began breeding in their third year, but 15·7 per cent started in their second, and a few, 1·6 per cent, in their first. In general the birds returned to the same colony each season, and even to the neighbourhood of the same spot. This tendency seemed to increase with age, and less than ten per cent of the birds taken on three or more seasons were found on different sites. The older birds were also the first to begin breeding each summer and were more inclined to attempt to renest on the same place if they lost their eggs. They thus had a stabilizing effect on the group as a whole and increased its breeding efficiency. It would appear that in a colony consistently occupied by the same birds clutches are abandoned less readily, incubation and the care of the chicks are carried on more steadily and the resultant yield of fledglings is larger.

The British terns normally spend the winter on coasts much farther south, from Spain to the Antarctic. The Little Tern travels the shortest distance, and the Arctic, which winters in the Antarctic, the longest. Sandwich, Common and Roseate Terns all occur in South African waters during the southern summer. Some seem to stay to breed. I found Roseate Terns nesting on an island in Algoa Bay at the beginning of November, and was assured that Common Terns habitually occupied the same site two months earlier in the year. Migrating birds start leaving the British Isles about the end of July and the majority are away by the beginning of September.

Terns have relatively few enemies apart from the usual trio of gulls, rats and men, though in the north the skuas will harry them for the food that they are carrying. On the whole the birds breeding in Britain are now faring well, particularly where their nesting-grounds have been protected. The growth of bungaloid settlements on previously deserted coasts sometimes displaces the Little Tern, but often the birds merely move to another site. During the recent war a few colonies of the larger terns were more disturbed by aircraft, particularly when they were used for machine-gun practice, but in most cases the birds do not seem to have deserted them. The Sandwich, Common and Roseate Terns all decreased markedly towards the end of the last century, but have since recovered most of the lost ground. This has been particularly noticeable in the case of the Roseate Tern, which ceased to breed in the Clyde area, Ireland and the Scilly Isles, but has since recolonized Ireland, where there are now over a dozen nesting areas.

Tern, or tarn, is of Scandinavian origin and probably comes from the Old Norse *therna*: it cannot be said to have any meaning beyond its present one. In Welsh, *morwennol*, and certain of the Germanic languages these birds are known as sea swallows, from their form in the air and the manner of their flight. In Scotland and the north, terns, the immature Kittiwake and the Common Guillemot are sometimes given the name of tarrock. This, with its alternative renderings terrick and tirrock, is probably derived from the Greenland Eskimo word *tâterâq*, which would seem to be imitative of their call.

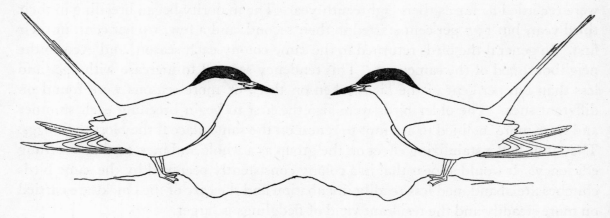

The Scavenging Gulls

THE gulls, with forty-three species, form as large a group as the terns. Like the latter they are gregarious and essentially coastal birds, but their geographical distribution is markedly different. They are completely absent from many parts of the tropics and their area of greatest concentration lies in the temperate zones. Many do not move far towards warmer waters during the winter months.

Gulls are fairly conspicuous and certain of them have habits that bring them to the attention of even the most casual observers. They are relatively fearless and scavenge readily. They are plentiful round harbours and, in coastal waters, behind ships at sea. As a result they are probably better known by sight than any other group. To many people they seem to be the only sea birds that deserve the name. Once, on a coral-fringed island where we had thousands of frigate-birds, boobies and noddies, I was asked why there were no sea birds in the tropics.

Six species breed in the British Isles. In considering them it is most reasonable to divide them into three groups, two containing individual birds, to be outlined later, and one comprising the remaining four. These four, whose portraits are given on the following page, are all typical members of the family. In form they are moderately large, with long wings, almost square-cut tails and fairly short legs. They have stout, wedge-shaped bills, with the upper mandible hooked at its tip and the lower conspicuously angulated on its lower edge.

The Herring Gull, *Larus a. argentatus*, is the most widespread and the best known. It is a fairly large bird with a wing span of about fifty to fifty-four inches. In summer the adult has the whole plumage snowy white, except for the back and dorsal surface of the wings, the greater part of which are a pale blue-grey. The wing has a narrow white border along its hind edge, and a triangular brownish black tip, marked with white spots or mirrors, composed of a decreasing extent of the outer five primaries. The bill is deep yellow with a bright vermilion blotch on the gonys. The iris is pale lemon-yellow, with the eyelids and orbital ring orange. The legs and feet are flesh-pink. The general colouring is pleasing, but the bird's appearance is spoilt by its rather heavy bill and the strained, rapacious set of its head. It is quick and alert in its movements, but it gives the impression of watching the world intently, not for its interest, but merely so that it shall not miss anything that might be seized and eaten. The winter plumage differs by the addition of a varying amount of brownish mottling on the head and neck, which makes it look dirty and untidy. This is particularly noticeable in August and September, when many have acquired their winter head markings but have not moulted the worn and battered wing and tail feathers.

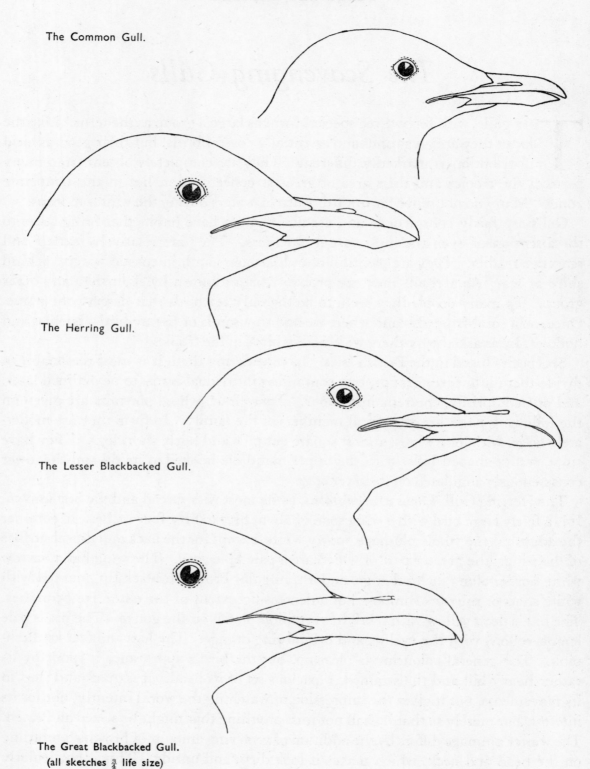

The Common Gull.

The Herring Gull.

The Lesser Blackbacked Gull.

The Great Blackbacked Gull.
(all sketches ¾ life size)

The Common Gull, *L. c. canus*, is the least plentiful of these birds in the south throughout the breeding season and is rarely seen in English waters, except off Dungeness in Kent. In the colder months a great number of winter visitors come over from northern Europe and during this time it is more plentiful than the two Black-backed Gulls together. Its colouring is very similar to that of the Herring Gull, but it is much smaller, with a wing span of about forty inches. Its bill is more slender, and the set of its head and body softer, so that it has a more attractive and refined appearance. The principal colour differences are in the soft parts. In the adult the legs, feet and bill are all greenish yellow, and the latter has no blood mark on the lower mandible. The iris is usually brown, fawn or yellowish white. The mantle is rather darker and the wings, relatively longer, project farther beyond the tail when the bird is at rest. In winter plumage the head is frequently more heavily spotted than in the Herring Gull.

The two Blackbacked Gulls resemble each other fairly closely. The smaller, *L. fuscus graellsii*, is slightly smaller than the Herring Gull, though the difference is not always discernible in the field, and to some extent the measurements overlap. According to my tracings the wing span ranges from forty-eight to fifty-two inches. The general colour is white, with the back, mantle and wings a dark slate-grey, the latter white-bordered and black-tipped in much the same manner as the Herring Gull. The soft parts are similar, except that the legs and feet are bright yellow. The Lesser Blackbacked Gull is a bold, aggressive bird, with many of the mannerisms of a natural bully. It frequently mixes with the Herring Gull, but, in feeding, often remains a little aloof until it sees something that it really wants. Then it moves in and takes it with ease and assurance.

The Great Blackbacked Gull, *L. marinus*, has a wing span of about sixty-three inches. Its colouring resembles that of the preceding species except that the back, mantle and wings are darker, almost black, and the legs and feet the bluish flesh colour of a corpse. This is the proudest and most rapacious of the British scavenging gulls. It has the aloofness and easy carriage of an individual always sure of getting its own way. It makes considerable slaughter among the sea birds round it, but it kills, not half apologetically as the smaller species seem to, but as though all its actions are covered by a divine mandate. If Marlowe had written *The Parliamente of Fowles* he would have made this bird or the Great Skua his supreme figure.

The Common and Herring Gulls are seldom seen far from land, except when they have been drawn away by ships. The two Blackbacked Gulls, especially the smaller, may be met with, particularly in spring and autumn, but even they are scarcely truly marine birds. The typical habitat of all four is the immediate neighbourhood of the shore-line, with their favourite feeding-places beaches and estuaries. The Herring and Lesser Blackbacked Gulls habitually carry this to its logical conclusion, and scavenge freely round harbours, refuse dumps and sewage outlets. On the whole they are not often found far inland during the summer, except in the case of the Common Gull, which in the north frequently inhabits freshwater lochs and may breed on open moorland at some distance from the sea. In the winter months food or good roosting-places on freshwater lakes sometimes bring the three smaller species well in from the coast, and large numbers have been recorded from some of the reservoirs in south-eastern England.

Their flight is powerful and buoyant. Normally the wings are not extended fully, but are held with the joints slightly flexed, thus accentuating the lines of the individual units. The beats are regular, strong and rather leisurely. They glide frequently, and make the most of any wind eddies behind ships or in the neighbourhood of cliffs and piers with an easy, captivating grace. The Herring Gull particularly is a master of movement in the air, and when food is being thrown to it hovers and dives with considerable skill. It may well be taken as the bird to whom Edwin Muir addressed his poem,

> . . . *walking upon the air,*
> *Like a schoolboy running and loitering, leaping and springing,*
> *Pensively pausing, suddenly changing your mind*
> *To turn at ease upon the heel of a wing-tip.* . . .

The scavenging gulls stand and walk easily, with the body parallel with the ground. They alight frequently and will settle on almost any solid object, but they like, if possible, to be a little above the level of their surroundings so that their quick eyes can watch the whole scene about them. When on the alert they keep the head well up, with a chest-forward, shoulders-back stance, like a regimental sergeant-major on parade. When at rest they flex the neck, dropping the head down till the nape meets the line of the back. In this position they seem to sleep, but the idea of repose is often belied by the frequency with which one lid is half raised. They usually roost in company, even outside the breeding season, and very large numbers, running into tens of thousands, have been recorded from favourite sites.

Their food is very varied and they appear to eat anything edible that they can get. In the winter months it consists mostly of all manner of shore organisms, occasionally small birds and mammals, and any available refuse. In the breeding season they also take the eggs and young of any birds that are near them, including their own species. Some, particularly the Great Blackbacked Gull, prey fairly heavily on the adults of the other colonial sea birds, including the Puffin, Shearwater and Storm Petrel. If it is not hurried when dealing with these birds it usually begins at the belly and turns the whole skin inside out, cleaning it as neatly and effectively as if it were preparing it for preservation. The Common Gull frequently catches insects, and all, though principally the larger species, take fresh fish. The Great Blackbacked Gull, and to a lesser extent the Lesser Blackbacked and Herring Gulls, are common visitors to the North Sea fishing-grounds in the autumn.

Much of the food is scavenged from the shore or the land. All paddle on wet sand or mud to bring worms to the surface. Insects are usually taken off the ground or the water, but they may be caught on the wing and even the Great Blackbacked Gull has been seen hawking a swarm of flying ants. Food on the sea is usually taken by alighting on the surface and swimming up to it, but it may be picked up as the bird swoops past. Diving from the air, with complete or partial submersion, has been recorded for all four species, though it does not seem to be a frequent occurrence. The most interesting particular habit is that of the Herring Gull, which drops molluscs or hermit crabs on to the ground from a height of fifteen to twenty feet to break their shells. This enterprising bird also becomes most adept at catching rabbits, and could not, therefore, have been popular with Sir J. Arthur Thomson.

The scavenging gulls produce a number of loud, rather strident calls, most of which are best described as mewing or wailing notes. When their nests are threatened they frequently fly round overhead emitting a continuous clucking, grumbling *kwuk-kwuk, kwuk-kwuk.* . . . Basically these calls are fairly similar in all four species. If one takes the Herring Gull as a standard one finds that in the Common Gull they are shriller, in the Lesser Blackbacked Gull deeper and louder, and in the Great Blackbacked Gull still deeper, as though it was a single voice maturing.

The Common Gull usually nests in small to medium-sized colonies. Typically these are situated on low rocks or small islands in lochs, but they may be on or near the sea-shore or on open moorland some distance from the coast. The Herring Gull usually nests on broad cliff ledges or the grassy tops of small marine islands, but it may make use of shingle beaches or occur among sand-dunes. It is generally gregarious, but single nests are not uncommon. The Lesser Blackbacked Gull is usually colonial, and may be found nesting with, or close to, assemblies of the Herring Gull. It also breeds on moorlands and freshwater islands a short distance from the sea : like the Common Tern it has bred as far inland as the Nottingham sewage farm, but this is exceptional. The Great Blackbacked Gull nests in much the same places as the Lesser, but it is less gregarious and isolated pairs, or small scattered groups, occur fairly often. It also generally chooses an elevated site, or one with a prominent rock near it from which one bird can keep watch.

Much of the sexual display of these birds is communal and, like the Cormorant, Gannet and Fulmar, their reproductive activity seems to be heightened by the presence of others near them. As a result, though they eat eggs and young from each other's nests, breeding is more efficient in colonies than among individual pairs. A certain communal feeling runs all through their breeding cycle and to some extent includes nearby groups, even when they are of different species. On Skomer I found that some of the Herring Gulls nesting on the cliff edge always joined in when the Blackbacked Gull colony on the top of the island was invaded, and the birds rose in the air to protest. In the same way I once saw a pair of Herring Gulls, who were mobbing a seal swimming too near a floating chick, assisted by a large group of Lesser Blackbacked Gulls. As soon as the seal moved away the parents quieted, and when they did so the other gulls flew off.

These birds usually build a moderately large nest of any suitable material, seaweed, heather, grass or sticks, that is easily accessible. The eggs are laid in May or early June. A normal clutch contains three. The colouring is fairly similar in all four species. The ground colour ranges from stone-buff to olive-brown and, in the smaller birds, umber. It is fairly thickly blotched and spotted with deep blackish brown or umber-brown and ash-grey. The eggs are laid at intervals of two days, and if taken are replaced. Occasionally eggs, mostly later ones, are paler and bluer, and may be unmarked. Both birds incubate. The duration of the incubation period is difficult to ascertain as it may begin with the appearance of the first, second or third egg. In the Herring Gull it lasts about twenty-seven days.

The eggs usually hatch at intervals of two days. The chicks are entirely covered with a thick, long, soft down, buffish grey with blackish brown spots on the upper surface, and paler and unmarked on the lower surface. The young are fed by both parents. They stay in the nest for the first few days. Later they wander away to any available cover. When approached they usually freeze and in this manner escape detection, but the young of the Great Blackbacked Gull are rather more independent and frequently attempt to run away. They fly when about seven weeks old, but can swim easily at a much earlier age if frightened into the water.

The first juvenile plumage in the Herring and Lesser Blackbacked Gulls is light umber-brown mottled with dark, blackish brown: the young of these two species cannot be distinguished in the field with surety until the mantle has begun to attain its adult colouring. In the Common Gull the plumage is fairly similar on the dorsal surface, with the forehead, throat and base of the tail whitish, and the breast and belly whitish mottled with brown. In the Great Blackbacked Gull it is like the Common Gull, except that the ground colour of the upper parts is paler and the markings relatively smaller and more clearly defined. The young birds are not fed to any great extent after they can fly, though they may continue to solicit for food, with occasional success, for some time.

The full adult plumage is not attained until the bird's third year in the case of the Common Gull, and its fourth in the other three species. The change in the intervening period is a gradual one, the white areas clearing slowly with each moult. Detailed accounts have been published describing the plumage at each stage, but recent work by H. H. Poor in America on the Herring Gull has shown that in this species there is considerable individual variation, and that in most cases it is impossible to determine a bird's age accurately, in the field or in a museum, by its colouring. Males also appear to mature more rapidly than females. At present no comparable work has been done in Britain or on the other scavenging gulls,

Above : A Great Blackbacked Gull on its nest, taken on Puffin Island off the coast of Anglesey.
Below : A Lesser Blackbacked Gull nesting among the bluebells on Skomer, Pembrokeshire.

The Greater blackbacked
Gull.

Above: a fully
fledged youngster,
about eight weeks old
Below: three newly
hatched chicks.

[74]

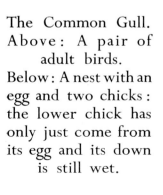

The Common Gull.
Above : A pair of
adult birds.
Below : A nest with an
egg and two chicks :
the lower chick has
only just come from
its egg and its down
is still wet.

[75]

The Herring Gull

Above: A worn and tattered bird at the end of the breeding season
Below: On its nest

The Herring Gull in the air, looking for food, and below, diving for it.

Nesting Kittiwakes
Above. a colony on the cliffs at Herma Ness
Below: three birds on the Isle of May: two of the latter have their beaks open
and are panting from the heat of a full sun.

Nesting Kittiwakes
Above : with an egg and newly hatched chick.   Below : with two almost fully fledged youngsters.

A
gliding
Kittiwake
seen from
above.

Nesting Great Skuas
and two chicks,
three to four days old.

The sitting bird in the
bottom picture is
panting from the heat

[81]

The Great Skua in the air.
The top bird is calling to
its mate, the two lower ones
diving at an intruder
standing too near to its nest.

[82]

An Arctic Skua
turning in the
air.

A Great Skua
banking.

[83]

The Arctic Skua
Above : A dark phased bird alighting at its nest
Below . A pale bird sitting

but it is probable that his conclusions apply equally well to this country and to the Blackbacked Gulls at least. Immature birds frequently hang round harbours and other like scavenging points, but are seldom seen in the neighbourhood of the breeding grounds. In the Cornish fishing ports they form over half the gull population at all times of the year.

The birds usually begin to leave their nesting-sites in July, and the majority are away by the end of August. British Common Gulls generally spread over the Scottish and Irish coasts, while in England there is a large influx of winter visitors from Scandinavia and the Baltic. The Herring Gulls mostly disperse over home waters and, on the east coast, are augmented by visitors from the Continent. Some Lesser Blackbacked Gulls disperse, but the majority migrate south, wintering mostly along the Bay of Biscay and the Spanish coast; a small proportion, mostly juveniles, enter the Mediterranean, while others spread over the African coast as far as Senegal. Little direct information is available about the Great Blackbacked Gull; it is probable that some are sedentary or disperse in home waters, according to the food available, while others move south to the Bay of Biscay and the Spanish coast. In effect this means that though a proportion of the scavenging gulls breeding in the British Isles leave during the colder months, our winter population is at least as large as the summer one.

All four birds appear to be increasing steadily. This is particularly marked in the Common Gull, which began to multiply in Scotland and western Ireland in the last century and has since extended its range to north-east Ireland, Cumberland, Northumberland and Kent. The Herring Gull has increased considerably in Scotland, and probably elsewhere, but it has always been abundant. In this connection it is interesting to note that reports from the east coast of North America show that the Herring and Great Blackbacked Gulls are increasing in numbers and extending their range there also. The latter did not nest on the coast of Maine until 1928, but by 1942 there were breeding pairs on ninety-eight islands. In general it would seem that though these birds are subject to the depredations of the usual trio, gulls, rats and men, they are well able to look after themselves. Some of their most spectacular increases have occurred in areas which have been protected for the benefit of other birds: on the Isle of May in the Firth of Forth the gull population has risen from fifty pairs to nearly a thousand in twelve years. It would seem, in view of their marauding activities, that under such circumstances it would be quite justifiable to attempt to reduce their numbers again by a deliberate destruction of their nests. In America a flourishing colony of Herring Gulls has entirely replaced a large ternery on the Weepecket Islands in southern Massachusetts: in 1934 there were some 3,500 terns and no gulls: in 1942 1,000 gulls and no young terns.

Gull is derived from an old Celtic word for these birds, and is cognate with the Cornish *gullan* or *guilan*, the Welsh *gwylan* and the Breton *gwelan*. It probably came from a root meaning wailing or wailer, which has survived in *gwel-a*, to weep.

The Blackheaded Gull

THE Blackheaded Gull, *Larus r. ridibundus*, must be counted the least marine of the birds outlined in this book. The divers, the Common Eider, even the Oystercatcher, are all more closely associated with the coast than it is. It would probably not be included if it were not a gull. Many of its breeding-places are far inland and relatively few individuals are seen on the sea.

The Blackheaded Gull is one of the smallest of the British gulls, with a wing span of just under three feet. Its build, and particularly the shape of its bill, is lighter and less powerful than that of the scavenging gulls, and it lacks their harsh, vicious appearance. Its colour in the adult is similar in general to that of the greybacked species, but with several important minor differences, apart from the one from which it derives its name. The wing is a fairly uniform blue-grey, except for a thin band along the forward edge, broadening to include the greater part of the outer five primaries, which is white. The inner margins and tips of the outer primaries are black, with no white mirrors on them. The bill and feet are deep red. In some individuals the body feathers, especially on the breast, are gently suffused with a rose-pink blush, like those of the terns and tropic-birds, but this is not a constant characteristic.

In the breeding season the head is coffee-brown, with a white half-circle round the posterior border of the eye. Unfortunately this distinctive feature is lost in the winter plumage, which may be acquired as early as the end of July. Usually all that remains of it are a few dusky markings in the neighbourhood of the eye and, farther back, in the region of the ear. Moulting birds, which are frequent in July and August, show various degrees of patchy mottling on the head. Birds in their first summer plumage have a black subterminal band on the tail and a partial hood with a fair number of white feathers on the forehead and chin.

The flight of the Blackheaded Gull is lighter and more buoyant than that of the other British species, and it flaps its wings more quickly. It bears some resemblance to that of the Sandwich Tern and there is often a perceptible rise and fall of the body with each beat, but it is not so marked as in the tern.

The diet and feeding habits are very varied. Crustacea, worms and insects, in all stages, make up the greater part of it. Small fish, molluscs, young birds and eggs are also taken, together with seeds, plants and almost any form of edible garbage. It scavenges in the same manner as the other gulls, hawks for flying insects on summer evenings and occasionally dives for fish. It follows the plough like Rooks and Starlings for the larvæ that are turned up by it, and in spring and autumn may be seen trampling in the wet mud and sand of estuaries to bring the worms to the surface.

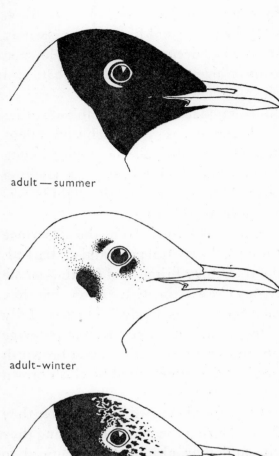

adult — summer

adult-winter

juvenile — first summer

juvenile — newly fledged

The Blackheaded Gull
(all sketches ¾ life size)

The Blackheaded Gull is a sociable bird and is usually seen in small groups, either with other members of its own species or with other birds. On shores and estuaries it generally mingles with waders and other gulls, while inland it is often in company with Rooks, Lapwings or Golden Plovers. It nests gregariously in colonies of varying size. Small units may be fairly scattered, but the larger colonies are generally tightly packed.

The nesting-sites vary considerably. Some of the largest colonies, as at Raven-glass, are on marram-covered sand-dunes near the shore. The favourite sites appear to be on the marshy edges of pools, small tussock islands in freshwater or on patches of floating weeds. These may be near the sea, but frequently they are far inland on open moors. In Yorkshire it breeds at a height of nearly 2,000 feet. It seldom occurs on marine islands except in Ireland, where there are several colonies off the coast of Antrim and County Down.

Birds usually arrive at the colony already paired. Feeding of the female by the male, followed by coition, has been recorded as occurring amongst couples on open ground as early as the first week of April. A great number of observations have been made on the sexual display of this species, particularly by F. B. Kirkman. The nest is an indifferent structure built of any available vegetable material. Its size and extent depend greatly on the amount in the immediate neighbourhood. In several cases recorded by Kirkman the site was selected and the work begun by the male, who was joined later by the female.

The eggs are laid, at intervals of twenty-four hours, in late April or early May. The normal clutch consists of three, but two are frequent, and four, five or six may occur. They usually vary from a light stone colour to a deep umber-brown, blotched and spotted with purplish grey and dark brown or black. Both birds incubate and the eggs take about twenty-three days to hatch.

Blackheaded Gulls are very noisy at their breeding-places. They call to each other at intervals all through the day and a considerable clamour is raised each time a new-comer alights at its nest. An interesting feature of this babel, also occurring among colonies of terns, is sudden complete silences following which all the birds rise in a cloud and fly round together as a compact flock. After a short time the flight breaks up and the birds return to their nests and their normal bickering.

The young chicks are covered with a thick, rather silky down. The dorsal surface is a dark golden buff with brownish black markings, the ventral paler and unmarked. They are normally fed by both parents, but the male may bring food for the female to pass on to them. For the first few days they stay close to the nest. After that they scatter if disturbed and readily take to the water, swimming freely. They are fully fledged in six to seven weeks, but may begin to fly earlier. The juvenile plumage differs from the adult in having the mantle an uneven brown, with some brownish grey on the wing coverts and the back of the head, and a subterminal blackish brown band on the tail.

Normally the parents continue to feed the chicks for about two months after they have hatched. Then they are left to themselves. During the period of feeding they are usually drawn away from the nesting-site and may ultimately be enticed to accompany the adults to their autumn quarters on shores or estuaries some distance away. On the other hand, at some places, such as the mouth of the Hampshire Avon, one seems to see only mature birds. Occasionally youngsters continue to solicit for food successfully for a much longer time. J. A. G. Barnes recorded an instance in *British Birds* in 1945 in which a pair remained together from August to February 18, when he lost sight of them. During this period the young bird apparently recognized its parents in flight and would begin bowing and whistling before the adult alighted. Occasionally the food was brought in the adult's bill, but usually feeding was by re-gurgitation, on land or on the water. The mature bird regularly drove off other Blackheaded and Common Gulls that approached too close to the youngster.

Some interesting observations were made on chicks hatched in an incubator. They were at first quite helpless and unable to feed themselves. They did not open their bills instinctively when touched or at the sight of food, but when a little was gently dribbled from a fountain-pen filler into the corner of the mouth they swallowed it immediately. After this had been repeated several times they opened their bills freely and cried loudly for more. The first thing that they learnt to recognize was the voice of the lady feeding them. By the end of the second day one word uttered in their vicinity was sufficient to start the whole company calling for food, even if they could not see her.

They were able to run easily by the end of the second day, but did not seem to recognize the nature of water until they were about a week old. When placed in a shallow dish they treated it like dry land and made no attempt to drink. One bird totally deprived of water until its tenth day bathed and drank on its first introduction to it.

Marked individual differences of temperament manifested themselves early. One soon became dominant over the remainder and quickly adopted a timid, ineffectual chick as its companion. All of them began to associate in pairs when they were about six weeks old. One chick, which unfortunately lost its mate, found a temporary substitute in a lump of cotton wool. They taught themselves to fly, and were able to do so about as soon as birds brought up under natural conditions.

The adult birds begin leaving their nesting-sites about the middle of July and most of them are away by the end of August. A small proportion migrate, and ringed birds have been recovered from the coasts of France and Spain and, in single instances, from the Azores and Senegal. The majority merely disperse over the British Isles, making their way to suitable shores (usually low-lying and cliffless), estuaries, harbours and other places where food can be obtained. They are always much in evidence along parts of the Cornish coast from early August onwards, though the nearest colonies of any size are in mid-Wales and Dorset. During the autumn and winter months they also frequent marshes, reservoirs, sewage farms and tidal rivers, well away from their breeding-grounds. They are particularly noticeable in certain river-side towns such as London, where they are easily the most plentiful species. A number of birds from Germany and the Baltic countries visit Britain, principally eastern England, for the winter, and some apparently stay to breed.

The Blackheaded Gull decreased considerably in numbers during the nineteenth century. In the fifty years before the war it showed a widespread increase, details of which were given in two papers by P. A. D. Hollom published in *British Birds* in 1940. It also appears to have extended its range in some areas of western Europe, and has colonized Iceland, where it first nested in 1910. In part its reduction in Britain was probably due to the elimination of nesting-sites, as a result of encroachment on the countryside, and the wholesale collecting of eggs for food. Collecting has continued in this century, the eggs usually appearing on the table as plovers' eggs, but on more careful lines.

The Kittiwake

THE Kittiwake, *Rissa t. tridactyla*, is the smallest, most marine and most attractive of the British gulls. It is rarely seen over the land, nests largely on inaccessible coastal cliffs and outside the breeding season disappears over the open sea. Unlike the other species it is able to drink salt water.

It has roughly the shape and colouring of a small Herring Gull, but it is softer and gentler in its lines. Sitting birds have a delicate, demure appearance that is quite lacking in the larger species. Even in repose the Herring Gull has the look of a brigand, while a nesting Kittiwake might be a well-pleased young woman, newly married.

The Kittiwake has a span of about thirty-five inches. In the adult the dorsal surface of the wing is bluish grey, with a thin white border along the posterior edge, and the tip black, as in the Herring and Common Gulls, but the grey is darker rather than paler over the mantle and the outer primaries have no white tips or mirrors. The bill is a uniform, slightly greenish yellow, the inside of the mouth and the orbital ring orange-red, and the legs and feet brownish black. The hind toe is vestigial and generally has no claw.

The Kittiwake is less noisy than the other British gulls, and its usual call, *kitti-waake, kitti-waake*, or a variation on it, highly distinctive. During courtship and the early stages of incubation the birds converse a great deal, and at all times a newcomer is greeted by its mate. Once they are well settled on their nests they are more at rest than the Blackheaded Gull, and, even in a tightly packed colony, there is little bickering. They are usually silent away from their breeding-grounds, though flocks fishing in rich water may, under the stress of excitement, become as voluble as terns.

The flight is swift and graceful. The Kittiwake has the quicker wing-beats of the Blackheaded Gull, but it bounces less and its course is more deliberate and ordered. It frequently follows ships, swinging behind them with wide down-wind glides that are a little reminiscent of the Cape Hen or the smaller albatrosses. In spite of its lightness its flight is powerful and it can manage well in a north Atlantic gale, provided that it is not caught on a lee shore, or exhausted by lack of food.

Its food consists chiefly of small fish and other organisms taken from the surface of the sea. These may be picked up as the bird passes, or it may settle on the water and then dive in the manner of the guillemots. It floats lightly and buoyantly, and swims well under water though it seldom submerges for long. Occasionally it dives by plunging from the air as the terns do. In this country, at least, it never feeds from beaches or dry land, and is never found scavenging in harbours with the larger gulls.

The Kittiwake.

head and right foot   (¾ life size)

The Kittiwake nests in small, compact colonies on ledges on precipitous sea cliffs or the walls of caves. Frequently the recesses chosen are very narrow and in some cases the rock face appears to be almost smooth. The birds are fond of the company of their own species and will pack closely in most unfavourable places, leaving broader ledges a hundred yards or so away untenanted. They do not seem to be disturbed by the presence of guillemots but, as on the Noup of Noss, they are easily elbowed away from their accustomed sites by Gannets or Fulmars.

The Kittiwakes come in from the sea to their breeding-places in March or early April. Nest building is a slow and leisurely performance, and it is seldom over before the middle of May. The finished structure is a beautiful piece of work. It is firm and strong, with a deep, well-defined cup. The principal material is seaweed, but mosses and grass are also used. The latter cannot be gathered from the sea, and the birds make foraging expeditions over the land to obtain them. On such occasions they usually move in small, compact flocks, as though they needed the comfort of each other's company to give them courage away from their natural element. They seem like children unwilling to walk alone through a dark wood.

Kittiwakes seldom alight on the land except at their breeding-ledges. The sexual display and coition usually take place on the half-finished nest. The eggs are laid at the end of May or in June. There are typically two in a clutch, but in England, from the Farne Islands southwards, there are often three, while in the Shetlands and farther north the birds frequently lay only one. The colour is very variable. All the usual gull shades may occur, though the ground colour is normally light and the brown blotches a warmer tone than in the other British species. The length is about 2·15 inches.

Both birds incubate and the eggs take about twenty-three days to hatch. The young chicks are covered with a thick, long, rather silky down. It is white on the underparts, and an uneven, dark greyish brown on the dorsal surface, except on the head, neck and tips of the wings, where it is creamy white. The young are fed by both parents with partially regurgitated food. As in the cormorants, the chicks have to meet it half-way, and put their heads and even necks into the adult's throat to search for it.

The young birds are fully fledged when about five weeks old. The juvenile plumage differs from the adult in having blackish mottling round the eye and over the ear, a broad black collar on the hind neck and a broad black terminal band on the tail. The back is also mottled with black, and there is a diagonal blackish bar across the wing to the wrist which is continued along the outer primaries. The bill is black, and the legs and feet dark brown. This colouring is retained, with small variations, until the bird's second autumn, when it acquires a plumage closely resembling that of a winter adult.

The nesting-sites are usually abandoned in August, but birds may remain in the vicinity until the beginning of October. Once away from the colonies they disperse over the open sea until the following season. Juveniles are mainly pelagic until they are two or three years old and ready to breed, though I have seen occasional individuals in the neighbourhood of the nesting-grounds in early summer. Most of the outward movement appears to be towards the south and west, but birds ringed in Britain have been recovered from the Faroes, the North Sea and the coast of Europe. Six birds in their second and third years have been taken in American waters from Greenland to Newfoundland: one ringed on the west coast of Greenland was recovered off Holland. There is, however, nothing to suggest that Kittiwakes habitually cross the Atlantic, though there is no doubt that birds from both sides mingle in mid-ocean, where they are fairly numerous from November to May, south of sixty degrees north latitude and north of a line from the Azores to Nova Scotia. It is probable that they normally return to breed in the colonies in which they were reared.

Kittiwakes are seldom molested at their nesting-sites. In their vicinity they are liable to attack from skuas, in the north, and the Great Blackbacked Gull. They appear to have increased in Scotland since the beginning of the century, but not in the south. A colony that I saw on Grassholm this year was much the same size and shape as in a photograph taken over sixty years earlier.

Kittiwake is derived from their typical call. In Scotland and the north immature birds are frequently known as Tarrocks, a name that is also applied to the terns and the Common Guillemot. It is probably derived from the Greenland Eskimo *tatarrok* or *tâterâq*.

The Skuas

THE skuas form a small family of largely dark or dull brown birds, closely related to the gulls. Like the latter they are essentially inhabitants of the colder temperate zones, and occur both north and south of the equator. A point of difference is that they all move to much warmer climates during the winter months. As a result the flight ranges of the northern and southern groups overlap, and in parts of South America and South Africa one meets Arctic skuas during the summer months and Antarctic ones during the winter.

The skuas are fairly large birds with powerful, thick-set bodies, stout, hooked beaks, and long, well-developed wings. The feet are webbed, and the legs short and stout. The birds fall naturally into two groups, each represented by a species breeding in the northern parts of the British Isles. One contains the larger, heavier birds, who have short, almost square-ended tails. The other, slighter in build and more pleasing in their general proportions, have rather long, wedge-shaped tails with, in the adult, the central pair of feathers considerably elongated.

The skuas are essentially predatory. Their position among sea birds is analogous to that of the hawks among land birds, the larger skuas corresponding to the buzzards or smaller eagles, and the smaller ones to the falcons. The main diet of the British species is fish, the greater part of which is obtained from other birds. Gannets, gulls and terns are attacked in the air and forced to disgorge their recent meals. In this method of hunting they bear a marked resemblance to the tropical frigate birds. Like the latter they will also pick fresh fish from the surface for themselves. On land they kill large insects, mammals and birds of suitable size, and take young birds and eggs. They are said to attack young lambs and will feed on offal and sheep's placentæ in the manner of Ravens.

The skuas usually breed on high, open grassland, fairly near to the sea. They form sparse, scattered colonies, with each nest in the centre of a small territory which the parent birds defend fiercely. Outside the breeding season they wander some distance from the coast and at such times are essentially more marine than the majority of the British gulls. In the south Atlantic I have seen skuas over four hundred miles from the nearest land.

The Great Skua, *Stercorarius s. skua*, is a bulky bird, with a weight of about 3½ lb. and a wing span of fifty-four inches. Its colouring is variable. Usually the upper surface is a dark greyish brown, streaked with pale yellowish brown on the neck and back : the lower surface is slightly paler in tone and more rufous in tint. The basal portions of the inner webs of the primaries are white. These areas are not visible when the bird is at rest, but in the air they form a conspicuous white triangle. The bill, legs and feet are black, and the irides dark brown.

The Great Skua was at one time nearly extinct in the British Isles and was reduced to a few pairs breeding on Unst at the north end of the Shetlands. Some measure of protection was afforded to it, through the efforts of the Edmonstones of Buneness, and it now occupies two large areas on Unst, and has spread to other islands in the same group, Fair Isle and Hoy in the Orkneys. In some localities it is threatening to displace the Arctic Skua. The earliest arrivals reach the nesting-grounds at the beginning of April, but the numbers are not complete until the middle or end of May. A considerable proportion of the later comers are non-breeding birds, who spend the summer in a loosely knit group, roosting on suitable hillocks somewhere within the colony.

Great Skuas are very fond of drinking and bathing in fresh water. Small groups of them can always be seen round the edge of any lochans within the limits of the colony. They wash by walking slowly into the water up to their bellies, and then rolling their bodies from side to side to throw it over their backs. Sometimes they submerge completely and they have been seen lying on their backs in the water, with their feet in the air.

The characteristic posture of these birds, used by the Vikings to ornament their helmets, is with the head thrown up and the wings fully extended, pointing backwards and upwards. In this position they usually call harshly once or twice and then drop their wings. This stance appears to be adopted at all moments of excitement. It is the principal feature in the sexual display and is taken up by any new-comer to a group of resting birds. Usually it is not answered, but if it is both birds move towards each other, calling several times, until one retreats. They seldom fight, but seem to come to a rapid, tacit understanding of the superiority of one over the other. When feeding from carrion they frequently do so in sequence, the dominant birds first and the others later, in descending order.

The breeding birds slowly stake their claims to small territories, taking up their positions, as far as possible, on a knoll or slight prominence somewhere within it. Great Skua colonies are peculiar in that they seem to consist of a number of smaller units, each composed of six to a dozen or so pairs, separated by areas of unoccupied ground. The eggs are laid in a sparsely lined, fairly deep depression in heather, grass or dry moss. The normal clutch consists of two, but three and four, possibly the work of two hens, have been recorded. The eggs are gull-like, with a length of about 2·75 inches. The usual ground colours are olive-grey or reddish brown, with the markings more numerous towards the broader end.

The eggs are laid at intervals of two days. Both birds incubate. The one not on the nest usually keeps watch twenty to thirty yards away. If one approaches too near to the area it rises into the air with a harsh shriek, which ultimately draws its

The Arctic Skua.
(⅖ life size)

The Great Skua.
(⅖ life size)

companion to it. Once on the wing they circle round, grumbling to each other. Then if one moves closer they begin a systematic attack. Sometimes they swoop straight at one's head from a considerable height. More usually they dive some distance away and then glide, with half-raised wings, parallel to the ground. In either case they begin by dropping to a height of about five feet and then sweep upwards when only a few yards away, lowering their feet as they do so. Usually they swoop from one direction only, but some birds fly backwards and forwards on a shuttle service. The attack may be silent, or accompanied by a harsh shriek of *kark-kark*. The speed that they attain is considerable. There is little doubt that they aim at frightening the intruder rather than injuring him; the effect is like that of Japanese dive-bombing. One is not likely to be hit, but the difficulty lies in assuring oneself in advance that one is not going to be.

Incubation takes about four weeks and the eggs hatch at intervals of two days. The young chick is covered with a long, rather silky down, buff-grey in colour with a faint suggestion of a pinkish bloom on it. For the first few days they are brooded by the female and fed by the male. Later both birds bring food and the chicks wander from the nest into the nearest available cover. They are fully fledged in six to seven weeks. The juvenile plumage is fairly similar to that of the adult, but darker and duller.

The Great Skuas begin to desert their nesting-grounds about the middle of August

95

and most of them are usually away by the end of September. According to Lawrence Bruce the non-breeding birds are among the earliest to leave. The youngsters seem to remain in the vicinity of their nests, still being fed by their parents, until three to four weeks after they are fully fledged. Then they go straight out to sea with them. One rarely sees deserted fledglings, or young birds searching for food on their own, in the neighbourhood of the colony.

Autumn, winter and early spring are spent at sea. The main dispersal is west and south-west, into the north Atlantic. The Great Skua does not breed regularly in America, but it is fairly plentiful on the fishing-banks off Newfoundland during the winter months and may occur as far south as Nantucket. A smaller number of birds pass down the east coast of Britain. A few of these remain to winter in the North Sea and the Great Skua is fairly common on the herring fishing-grounds off East Anglia in the autumn. The majority travel on at least as far as the open waters off the Iberian peninsula and the west coast of Africa.

The Arctic Skua, *S. parasiticus*, is slighter and smaller than the Great Skua, and more pleasing in appearance. Two distinct colour phases occur; and intermediate patterns, forming a shadowy third, are fairly common. The paler birds, who make up about twenty per cent of those breeding in the Shetlands, are a dark ash-brown, lighter on the belly, with the sides of the head and neck straw-yellow and the chin and breast dull white. In the darker phase the upper surface is dark ash-brown and the neck and underparts a slightly lighter, sooty brown. Intermediate birds are frequently markedly paler below and have a trace of yellowish grey on the sides of the neck. The bill is always brownish black, and the legs and feet dull black. All phases interbreed freely.

The distribution of the pale and dark forms appears to be peculiar. One would have expected the lighter birds to become relatively more numerous as one moved northwards, and L. S. V. Venables has estimated that about seventeen per cent of the birds breeding in the Shetlands, twenty per cent in the Faroes, twenty-seven per cent in south Iceland, forty-two per cent in north Iceland, and fifty per cent at Varanger are of this form. Other authorities have found seventy-five per cent pale in western Greenland, over ninety per cent in Spitzbergen, and over ninety-five per cent on Bear Island. On the other hand the dark form is rarely seen on the Outer Hebrides, and recently David Lack has calculated that twenty-five per cent of the birds breeding on Papa Westray and forty-five per cent on Hoy, both in the Orkneys, are of the light phase. It would appear that the darker birds become relatively less numerous as one moves outwards from the Shetlands, reaching their minimum to the south on the outer Hebrides and to the north on Bear Island and Spitzbergen.

The flight is lighter and more graceful than that of the Great Skua, and the wings relatively longer. The birds ride with an easy buoyancy and glide frequently. The beats are regular and unhurried. When chasing their prey they are as agile as the frigate birds, and follow every turn and twist of the victim perfectly. If Great Skuas pass over their nesting territory they attack them readily. At such times they appear to be able to fly much faster and to be their masters. Their manner of alighting is different. The Great Skuas come down with their wings raised vertically and often pause in an attitude rather like that of their display posture. The Arctic Skuas keep their wings out sideways, like a gull, and frequently begin to fold one before the other. They never stand with them extended upwards.

Much of the sexual display seems to take place on the wing, when the birds perform an amazing series of aerial acrobatics. Non-breeding birds do not hang round the colony in a loose group as they do in the Great Skua, and they are in general much less communal in their behaviour. I have never seen Arctic Skuas drinking or bathing in fresh water.

Their characteristic call on the breeding-grounds is a long mewing note, rather like the cry of a kitten. They swoop at intruders near the nest, but less frequently and less persistently than the Great Skua. They generally attack from behind or the side instead of in front. Their call at such times is often a soft, toneless *tik-a-tik-tik*, repeated several times. Commonly when the nest is threatened one bird feigns injury, tumbling about on the ground and wailing a short distance away. At intervals it rises in the air and then comes down again, crying and trailing its wings as before.

Much of the rest of the breeding sequence is similar to that of the larger birds. The eggs are smaller (about 2·25 inches long) and frequently darker. The incubation period is usually a day or two shorter and the young birds develop more quickly. The juvenile plumage differs markedly from that of the adult, both in colour and in having the centre tail-feathers no longer than those on either side of them. In the lighter birds the upper surface is a dark greyish brown, spotted with buff on the back, and the head and underparts dull buff barred with sooty grey. In the darker phase the young birds are a sooty, greyish brown, barred with buff on the rump, flanks, breast and belly.

After they are fledged the young Arctic Skuas appear to collect in groups of similar plumage pattern. Unlike the young Great Skuas they fly freely round the colony and can often be seen attempting to obtain food on their own, though there is nothing to show that they are successful, long before they leave for the open sea. The earliest birds begin to move away in August, but the exodus may not be complete until October. Most of them move down the east coast of Britain. The majority pass on to semi-tropical waters, some travelling as far as South Africa. The remainder spread over the North Atlantic. A few observations of individual birds would suggest that they return each year to breed in the same colony.

Skua is a Norwegian word from the Old Norse *skúfr*, Icelandic *skūmr*, meaning a skua or brown gull. The words are probably derived from a root for dull or dusky (Icelandic *skūmi*, Swedish and Norwegian *skum*).

The Razorbill

THE Razorbill is the first of four birds to be outlined in this book belonging to a group known collectively as the auks, and closely related to the extinct Great Auk. They are all small birds with short necks, rather squat bodies, very short tails and small, narrow wings. Their feet, which have only three toes, are large, webbed and placed far back, near the base of the tail, so that on land they habitually adopt an almost upright posture. They are confined to northern temperate waters and in many ways occupy a position analogous to that of the penguins in the southern hemisphere.

The four British auks, the Razorbill, the Common Guillemot, the Black Guillemot and the Puffin, are very similar in many of their habits and characteristics. They are essentially marine birds, coming ashore, initially with some reluctance, only to lay their eggs and rear their young. Outside the breeding season they normally frequent the open sea or off-shore waters out of sight of land, and only storm-driven birds are seen during the winter months.

Their flight is laboured and, except on their way to off-shore feeding-grounds, usually of short duration. The wings are moved rapidly with a peculiar whirring motion, so that they seem to vibrate rather than to beat. They seldom glide, except when alighting or diving down from their breeding-places. They travel low over the water and, except in the case of the Black Guillemot, are frequently met with in small parties, strung out in Indian file or echelon. When alighting they usually sweep up to the landing-place in a long curve, with their tails fanned and their feet spread out. As they approach the spot their shoulders are thrown back until their bodies are almost vertical. At the last moment they perform a back-pedalling movement of their wings, so that they finally drop like an ungainly helicopter landing on a city roof. The whole process seems to cause them considerable anxiety, and they frequently fly past the spot on which they are going to alight several times before attempting to leave the air.

When coming down on the water they usually strike the surface breast and bill foremost, and then lift the head sharply as the splash begins to rise. They are very buoyant and float high on the water, like the Fulmar and the Manx Shearwater, not with the back and tail almost awash as the penguins, cormorants and divers do. They dive quickly but flurriedly, with a kick of their legs and a flick of their partly opened wings. Once submerged they swim well and much faster than on the surface. They drive themselves forward with their wings and steer with their feet, like the penguins.

The British auks feed largely on small fish, crustacea and marine worms. The food

adult

juvenile.

The Razorbill (¾ life size)

is caught under the water and swallowed before the bird emerges. Of this mixture fish usually comprises less than half of the adult's menu. The nestlings are fed almost exclusively on small fry which are carried back in the parent's bill. The Guillemot holds the fish lengthwise, with the tail drooping from one angle of its bill, and takes only one at a time. The Razorbill and Puffin carry the fish across the bill and generally bring back five or six at once. The maximum recorded is twelve, by a Razorbill, but I am sure that I have seen Puffins with more.

The British Razorbill, *Alca torda britannica*, is a neat, dapper little bird with a wing span of about twenty-five inches. In summer the head, neck and upper parts are a glossy jet-black, with a narrow white line from the bill to the eye and white tips to the secondaries. The underparts are snow-white, except for the coverts over the base of the primaries and secondaries, which are greyish brown. The bill, which is large and conspicuously flattened from side to side, is black with a curved white band on each side. The inside of the mouth is lemon-yellow, the irides dark brown and the legs and feet black. The winter plumage is fairly similar to the summer except that the chin, throat and sides of the face are white, there is no white line on the face, and the black of the upper parts is tinged with sooty brown.

The Razorbill is heavier and more thick-set than the other British auks, and has a relatively larger head. As a result, though slightly shorter than the Common Guillemot, it appears much the same size when floating on the water. It often shows a little of the lemon-yellow skin of its mouth at the angle of its bill, so that from a short distance the latter seems to have a horizontal pale band as well as a vertical one. It is restless and on land frequently moves its head from side to side.

According to J. M. Dewar the Razorbill is essentially a longshore diver. From an analysis of four hundred and seventy-one dives he decided that it preferred a depth of about seven feet and a submersion of twenty-two seconds. A bird in eighteen feet of water only reached the bottom, where it normally feeds, once in seven attempts, while the longest recorded dive was fifty-two seconds.

The Razorbill is a sociable bird and usually breeds in large, fairly congested

99

colonies. Like the Common Guillemot, with which it frequently associates, these are generally situated on steep, isolated sea cliffs. It differs in the type of position chosen, preferring to breed under the cover of broken rocks or in a crack or crevice. It never utilizes the bare tops of stacks, and may even nest on low shores if there is sufficient rocky cover.

The birds begin to return to the neighbourhood of their breeding-grounds in February; but they seldom start to come ashore before the end of March in southern England and as late as early May in the Shetlands. In the south most of the eggs are laid during the second half of May. Normally they are single, but clutches of two have been recorded. The egg is pear-shaped, though less markedly so than the Guillemot's, about 2·95 inches long and with a rough, granular shell. The ground colour usually ranges from a light coffee-brown to white, but occasionally it may be green. Over it is a fairly thick blotching or speckling, running from rich reddish brown to black. No nest is built and the egg is laid on bare rock.

Mated birds show a certain amount of affection for each other. They frequently touch or rub their bills together, and nibble at one another's heads and necks. When excited they adopt an ecstatic posture, with the bill pointing upwards and the wings half opened and thrust outwards and backwards, rather like an early riser stretching himself before his bath. When displaying sexually they rattle their mandibles together like castanets and vibrate the wings slightly. The partner responds by nibbling at the feathers of the throat. Often in the early stages of the breeding season the ecstatic stance is adopted when the mate is absent and for no apparent reason. During this period they frequently emit a long, grating, growling note: at other times they are usually silent.

The egg takes about four weeks to hatch. Both birds incubate. The young chick is completely covered with a thick, short, rather silky down, white on the face, crown and underparts, and mottled with white, buff and brownish black on the neck, back and wings. It is fed by both parents.

When the chick is about fourteen days old it leaves the nesting-site and flutters down to the sea. Usually it is stimulated to do so by its parents calling from below, but it may make the move on its own initiative. Its momentum carries it below the surface and it immediately swims freely under the water. If the shore is much beset by breakers it dives repeatedly until it is clear of them. As soon as it reaches calmer water it drinks liberally, and it may be that thirst is the principal factor that induces it to make the change on its own account. The parents, at first both and later one, remain near it on the sea for some time.

The first juvenile plumage resembles the adult winter plumage superficially, except that the chin, throat and sides of the head are usually deep brown. The bill, as shown in the line drawing, is much smaller. An interesting difference, which is only apparent on close examination, is that there are no flight or tail feathers. Their

Portrait of a Razorbill, taken on Skomer off the coast of
South Wales.

Razorbills
in the air

A Razorbill
with a downy chick
and below, a newly hatched chicken

[103]

All available space in use.   Above: Shags, Kittiwakes and Common Guillemots nesting on the cliffs of Staple Island, in the Farne Islands off the Northumbrian Coast.   Below: Common Guillemots on the face of the great cliffs of the Isle of May, in the Firth of Forth.   [10

Portrait
of a
Northern
Common
Guillemot,
taken on
Herma Ness
on the
Shetlands.

[105]

The Common Guillemot,
above, **three** birds one
bridled of the Northern
race incubating their eggs
on a cliff face in the
Shetlands, and below,
a pair of the Southern,
paler, race on Skomer
off the coast of Wales.

Southern Common
Guillemots with their chicks
on the Farne Islands,
and below,
a young chick
on Skomer.

Portrait of a Black Guillemot, or Tystie
taken on the island of Flottar in the Shetlands.

Puffins floating in the sea off the coast of Wales.

Black Guillemots
swimming off the
coast of Unst.

[109]

Puffin resting on Skomer

A Puffin
above, with a beakful of fish
for its chick, and below peeping
from the entrance of its nesting burrow

Gliding Puffins
seen from below
and the side.

place is taken by the upper coverts, and they do not start to grow until the first moult begins. The advantages of this condition, which occurs also in the Common Guillemot but not the other British auks, is not apparent, unless it is in some way associated with the young bird's early descent to the sea. The juvenile Puffin, which also has to flutter down to the water, does not do so until it is seven or more weeks old.

The Razorbills begin to desert their breeding-places about the middle of July and, in southern Britain, all are usually away by the middle of August. A few remain in the vicinity as late as October. The main movement is one of dispersal through home and European coastal waters, as far south as the Azores and the western Mediterranean. Relatively little successful ringing has been done, but a number of birds marked on Handa, off the coast of Sutherland, have been recovered from southern Norway, and birds from Skomer from the Atlantic and Mediterranean coasts of France.

Most of the Razorbill's breeding-places are fairly isolated and seldom troubled by man. In general its numbers have shown little change in the last hundred years.

Originally the full name of this bird was the Razorbilled Auk. Razorbill is self-explanatory. Auk was first applied to the Great Auk or Garefowl, and later transferred to the smaller species. Cognate forms exist in various northern languages, including the Icelandic and Swedish *alka* and the Danish *alke*, but apart from its obvious derivation from an Old Norse root its origin is obscure. Webster attempts to associate it with the Swedish *alle* (the Little Auk or Dovekie) and thence with the Greek *elea* (a marsh bird) or possibly *alkuōn* (the kingfisher), but though the latter was certainly assumed to be a sea bird the etymology seems rather forced.

The Guillemots

Two species of guillemot breed in the British Isles, the Common Guillemot, *Uria aalge*, and the Black Guillemot or Tystie, *U. g. grylle*. The former has many points in common with the Razorbill, with which it frequently associates during the breeding season. It is very plentiful and, especially in the north, is more numerous than its partner. The Tystie is less sociable than the other auks and is relatively scarce, occurring at the present time principally in northern and western Ireland and Scotland and the northern isles.

The Common Guillemot is slightly longer than the Razorbill and appears less neat and compact. It has a longer neck and a relatively smaller head. The bill is long and pointed, and the tail rounded instead of wedge-shaped. The birds breeding in Britain are divided into two races. The northern form, *U. a. aalge*, which occurs as far south as St. Abb's Head on the east coast and Islay on the west, has much the same colouring as the Razorbill, except that the head and neck are tinged with chocolate-brown, there are no white lines on the face and bill, the flanks are streaked with dark brown and the legs and feet are ochreous-grey. In the winter plumage the white on the cheeks is crossed by a thin dark line running back from the eye. The southern form, *U. aalge albionis*, resembles the northern except that the dark areas are markedly lighter and browner in summer and slightly browner in winter.

A varying proportion of birds, increasing as one moves northwards, have a white line round the eye which is carried backwards as a short white stripe. Birds thus marked are usually known as Bridled Guillemots. They do not appear to differ in any other respect from their fellows and breed freely with them. They must be accounted as no more than a colour phase, comparable to the pale form of the Arctic Skua. In southern England the proportion of bridled birds at most of the colonies is less than one per cent: in the Shetlands it is said to vary between 23·8 per cent and 26·4 per cent.

The Common Guillemot flies, swims and feeds in much the same manner as the Razorbill. When diving close to the shore it frequently chooses slightly deeper water, with an optimum of twelve to eighteen feet. Two hundred and ten dives recorded by J. M. Dewar had an average time of 25·7 seconds. The longest lasted 68 seconds, while the greatest depth was about 28½ feet. About half its food consists of fish, particularly sand-eels: the remainder is mostly crustacea, annelids and marine molluscs. Fish for the young are usually carried singly and lengthwise in the bill.

In southern England breeding birds begin to visit the nesting-cliffs at the end of December. The first inspection is very cursory and they soon return to sea again.

From then onwards they come back in increasing numbers at intervals until the end of April, when they start to settle down to a permanent occupation of suitable sites. Farther north they begin much later and the first visits may not occur until the middle of February. W. Aspden, assuming that females can be identified from year to year by the colouring of their eggs, has suggested that they usually find their way back to the same spot on the same ledge each season.

The Common Guillemot breeds in compact, and often large, colonies on the ledges of steep sea cliffs or the flat tops of isolated stacks. It seldom makes use of crevices, and in general chooses much more exposed sites than the Razorbill. It lays only one egg and makes no nest, though in April birds frequently toy with odd bits of material from abandoned nests of the Kittiwake. It is extremely sociable and favoured ledges are frequently grossly overcrowded. Guillemots are indeed so fond of each other's company that flying birds will attempt to alight on a rock top that is already over full, regardless of the fact that in doing so they knock two or three others off.

Mated Guillemots rub bills and nibble at each other's head and throat. They may even entwine their necks, and frequently bow to each other. They are very restless on their ledges and respond to any excitement, or anything that makes them uneasy, by twisting their heads rapidly from side to side and nodding them up and down. This almost constant movement continues throughout the breeding season. They are also very noisy on land, though silent at sea. The usual note is a prolonged, growling caw, which rises up from a large colony as a loud, undulating, grumbling murmur, like the cries of a stage crowd behind the scenes.

In the south the egg is usually laid about the end of May. It is markedly pyriform and about 3·2 inches long. The ground colour is very variable, ranging from a lovely deep blue-green, through white, to reddish brown. It is usually marked, thickly or sparsely, with lines or blotches of light straw-brown, bright red, sepia or black. Both parents incubate and the egg takes about four weeks to hatch. Brooding birds generally stand over their egg, or lie along it, with their backs to the sea and packed in tightly between their neighbours. In this position they look fairly comfortable and appear placid enough, but they are still restless and look round continuously to see what is going on.

The chick is entirely covered with a short, thick down, streaked with black and white on the head, throat and neck, sooty brown slightly spotted with brownish grey on the remaining upper parts and buffish white on the under surface. It is very vocal whenever it is disturbed or hungry, producing a repeated, squeaky cry of *weeoo, weeoo*. As it grows older this changes to a shriller double syllable, *quee-wee, quee-wee*. The chick is fed by both parents. In larger groups birds coming in from the sea sometimes give their fish to the youngster most insistent or nearest to them, irrespective of its relationship. This may be comparable to the communal feeding that occurs in the Gentoo Penguin, but it is probably no more than an accident

The Common Guillemot—Southern race.
(An adult from Skomer, Pembrokeshire, ¾ life size)

occasioned by the bird's un-easiness at the clamorous reception that it receives. Like the young Razorbill the chick leaves its ledge when about fourteen days old and flutters down to the sea, where it is tended by its parents.

The adults begin to aban-don the nesting-ledges at the end of July. They are usually completely empty by the middle of August in the south and the end of August in the north. The principal movement is one of dispersal and the majority do not appear to leave home waters, though they may wander some distance from their nesting-grounds.

The Black Guillemot differs from the Common Guillemot in a number of respects, and is frequently placed in a separate genus. It is smaller and tubbier, with a marked change between winter and summer plumage. It is much less sociable and is usually seen alone or in groups of two, three or four.

In appearance it is an attractive, but pot-bellied, inelegant little bird. In new summer plumage it is sooty black, with a large area on the upper wing coverts, the axillaries and under wing coverts white. In winter it is largely white, with the upper parts mottled with black, and the wings and tail the same colour as in summer. The bill is black, and the inside of the mouth and the feet vermilion.

In flight it whirrs its wings even more than the other British auks, and seems to buzz its way along, close to the water, like a giant bumble-bee. It often appears to have difficulty in taking off from the sea, and when disturbed in calm weather fre-quently dives in preference to flying. If at all uneasy when floating it repeatedly ducks its head under the surface. When submerged it swims well, using its feet almost as much as its wings. Twenty dives timed by E. M. Nicholson had an average duration of forty-five seconds, which is appreciably longer than Dewar's figure for the Common Guillemot. It is also more typically an inshore feeder, and usually dives in shallower water. Its food consists mostly of butterfish or rock-eels, molluscs and crustacea.

Its usual note is a shrill, feeble, rather whining whistle, *peeeeee*, which may termi-nate in a sigh as though all the cares of the world were on it. At other times the note is shortened and an almost *t* sound added at the end. In this form it is repeated again and again, so that the bird seems to twitter. The note is never noisy, but it is noticeable, and Tysties appear to be much less silent than the other auks individually. They call on the water and in the air, as well as at their nesting-places.

Birds begin to return to the waters near their nesting-sites towards the end of February, though they seldom start to land until late April or early May. The Black Guillemot never breeds in colonies, though several pairs may often be found a short distance away from each other. The eggs are usually placed under or among boulders on a rock-strewn beach, or deep in a crevice a short distance up a sea cliff. No nest is made. The birds are shy and retiring in their habits, and generally breed on small islands or lonely stretches of coast. When disturbed on their eggs they fly straight to the water and frequently make no attempt to return for several hours. When they do come back they usually swim cautiously towards the spot and then turn away again, advancing and retreating several times before they finally land.

The eggs are about 2·3 inches long, much smaller than those of the Common Guillemot, and almost a regular, blunt oval in shape. They are usually white, pale bluish green or buff, and spotted or blotched with blackish or reddish brown and grey. The normal clutch is two, though one is not infrequent. They are generally laid at the end of May or early in June. Both birds incubate and the eggs hatch in about three and a half weeks. Birds that are not brooding spend a fair amount of their time perched, singly or in groups of two or three, on nearby rocks at the edge of the sea. They usually begin by standing, with the whole length of the tarsi on the rock, and then, if not disturbed, sink down on their bellies, like cats balanced on a garden fence.

The young chicks are covered with a thick, soft down, a uniform sooty brown on the dorsal surface, paler on the ventral. They are fed by both parents with fish carried one at a time. These may be relatively large and are sometimes held, unsafely and rather inelegantly, by their tails, much like a butler taking out something that the cat has brought in. The chicks stay on their nests until fully fledged. The juvenile plumage resembles the adult winter plumage, except that the back is browner and the white patch on the wing spotted with black.

The Black Guillemot begins to leave its nesting-sites towards the end of July and most are away by the beginning of September. Some of them do not move far. The majority disperse over the waters round Scotland and northern Ireland, while a few drift farther south. The bird is mainly pelagic during this period, but occasionally single individuals make their way into odd bays and estuaries.

The Common Guillemot, like the Razorbill, is little troubled by man and its numbers have not altered much in recent years. The Black Guillemot, on the other hand, has grown much scarcer and seems to have withdrawn northwards. It has abandoned former nesting-grounds on the coasts of Yorkshire, east Scotland and north Wales, although occasional birds still turn up at these places and a single pair bred at Bempton in 1938.

Guillemot (which is now an English word and should have its last consonant sounded) was originally French and is probably a diminutive from *Guillaume*

(William). In which case the north-country name Willock and the sixteenth-century Wilmot should be regarded as having a similar origin. In Welsh the Common Guillemot is called *gwylog* and the Tystie *chwilog* (possibly from accommodation to *chwil*, whirling), which would appear to be related to the Celtic root for a gull. Bearing this in mind some authorities would derive guillemot from the Breton *gwelan* plus the Old French *mouette* (a diminutive from the Teutonic root for a gull), thus making the name into a cumulative compound consisting of a Celtic word for a gull explained by its Teutonic synonym. The Common Guillemot was also formerly known as the Murre, with alternative spelling Marre, Merre and Murr. The name has almost died out in Britain, but is still used frequently in America. Its origin is not known. It may be imitative of the murmurous noise of a large colony, or connected with Marrot, an equally obscure term which was formerly applied to all auks. It first occurs in Samual Purchas's *Purchas his Pilgrimage* in 1613, among a list of sea birds : its earliest definitive application to the Common Guillemot is in a description by John Ray, written in 1662. Tystie, which is the northern name for the Black Guillemot, has its origin in the bird's twittering note. This species is also sometimes called Dovekie (which should belong to the Little Auk) and Sea Pigeon, in reference to the soft, dove-like colour of its winter plumage.

The Puffin

THE Puffin, *Fratercula arctica grabae*, is an extraordinarily attractive creature with (though it is not suggested that there is necessarily any connection between the two points) a markedly human pose and mannerisms. It is surprising that it has not been used more frequently as a subject for illustrated books for children: it would lend itself readily to such treatment.

The Puffin is the last of the auks to be outlined in this book. It is fairly typical of the family in its general structure and colouring, but its appearance is highly characteristic, both in the great ornate bill-covering of the breeding season and in its shape. The Razorbill is compact, plump and neat, the Common Guillemot rather more sinuous and drooping, the Black Guillemot definitely pot-bellied, and the Puffin rotund and tubby.

In colour the Puffin is glossy black above and white beneath, with the under wing coverts a light brownish grey. The black of the hind neck is carried forward as a narrow black collar. Above it the throat, cheeks and a thin line to the nape are a soft, pale ash-grey in summer, darker, and almost blackish in front, in winter. The iris is a light grey, or hazel, brown. The orbital ring is a bright vermilion in summer, and dull orange-red in winter. The great, parrot-like bill is greyish blue at its base, vermilion at the tip and crossed with bars of yellow. The bare skin at the angle of the mouth is yellow. The horny covering of the bill is shed in winter, and the basic structure that remains is duller in colour, greyish brown at its base and chrome-yellow, rising to deep orange-red on the culmen, on the distal half. The legs and feet are vermilion at the beginning of the breeding season, dropping to orange-yellow in July and dull yellow in the winter months.

The Puffin is rather smaller than the Razorbill and Common Guillemot. It flies, swims and dives in much the same manner, though at all times its rounder body is noticeable. It stands and walks better than the other auks, keeping its tarsi erect instead of sinking on them at the first opportunity. Its gait has been well described by T. A. Coward as a nautical roll. It frequently stands upright for long periods, twisting its head slowly from side to side to watch all that is going on. When in company and at ease it usually rests on its abdomen, like the Black Guillemot. The Puffin has only one note, a low, growling *arr*, usually repeated three times, which may be emitted on land or on the sea.

It is a very sociable little bird and is generally seen in flocks of varying size. It breeds in thickly congested, and often large, colonies on grassy slopes, either above sea cliffs on the mainland or, where possible, on small marine islands. In England the

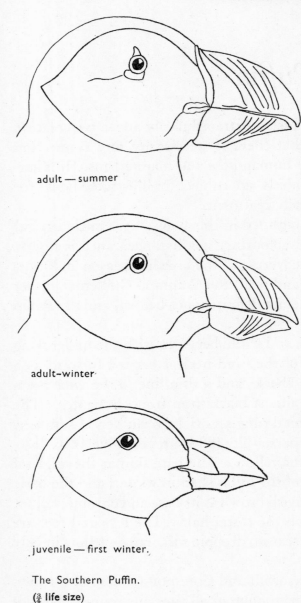

adult — summer

adult—winter

juvenile — first winter.

The Southern Puffin.
(¾ life size)

birds reach the vicinity of the nesting-grounds late in March and usually begin to land early in April. Like the other auks they congregate on the water for short periods and then disperse again to the open sea to feed, several times before they finally come ashore. The single egg is laid in a slight hollow at the end of an earthy burrow or, occasionally, in crevices among rocks. No real nest is built. The birds usually gather a few bits of grass and weed with which to line the depression, but drop most of it long before they reach it.

The burrow, which is usually two to three feet long, may be dug by the bird itself or taken over from a rabbit or a Shearwater. The Puffin is a good and doughty fighter, and will try to displace a previous occupant if it can thereby be saved the labour of digging for itself. The birds also fight among themselves for the possession of suitable holes, and one occasionally sees them rolling on the ground with their bills locked together.

The egg is normally laid during the first half of May. It is a round, blunt oval in shape and about 2·35 inches long. It is white in colour, but traces of purplish or brownish markings are frequently discernible, especially towards one end. Incubation takes about six weeks. It is presumed that both birds sit, but R. M. Lockley in twelve visits to eight nests always found the same bird present. He also often found the egg not attended in the day-time.

The young chick is entirely covered with a thick, long, soft down. It is a fairly uniform blackish to buffish brown, paler on the under surface. The chick is fed by both parents. At first it is given partially digested fish which is regurgitated for it. Later whole fishes are brought, carried several at a time, crosswise in the adult's bill. Usually the birds come ashore late in the afternoon, but Puffins have none of the Shearwater's reluctance to visit the land in daylight, and in isolated colonies individuals may be seen with their offerings at all hours. When the chick is fed on whole fish it excretes fairly lavishly, backing towards the mouth of its burrow and ejecting the material outwards. As a result there is usually a slightly whitened area round the entrance towards the end of the nesting season which serves, apart from the absence of the musty smell, to distinguish an inhabited Puffin burrow from one occupied by a Manx Shearwater, on the few islands where they occur together.

The youngster is abandoned when it is about forty days old. After a further week to ten days it makes its way to the sea by night, moving always downhill until it reaches the cliff-edge, where it flutters to the water. Like the other young auks it drinks freely, and then, diving frequently, paddles away from the land. The immature bird resembles the adult in winter plumage except that it is smaller, with a much smaller bill, and duller in colour. The upper parts are a dark brownish black, and the face a deeper, brownish grey.

In England Puffins begin to abandon the land in August, and have usually disappeared from the neighbourhood of their nesting-sites by the end of September. During the winter they are seldom seen in home waters, and appear to spend the period scattered over the open sea. Little is known of their movements at this time, but the dispersal appears to be a fairly wide one. A bird ringed on the coast of Sutherland and two from the Farne Islands reached Norwegian waters, while two nestlings ringed on St. Kilda in August 1939 were found off Newfoundland four months later. It is probable that Puffins normally return to their home colonies to breed each year, though a bird ringed in July in northern France was found nesting in the Scilly Isles two years later.

The Puffin's principal enemies are the scavenging gulls and, where they have reached its nesting-grounds, rats. It is still an abundant bird in some parts, but has decreased considerably in many colonies in the south, much as the gulls have increased in the same area. Puffins were at one time eaten, but this practice has long ceased. In the fourteenth century the annual rent of the Scillies was paid partly in Puffins.

Puffin appears to be an English word, later borrowed by the French, but it can only be traced back to the fourteenth century. Its origin, as Phillips suggested in 1706, is probably from puff, to puff out, "a bird supposed to be so called from its round belly, as it were swelling or puffing out", with the suffix denoting a diminutive. The Welsh name for it is *pal*, in spite of which an island off Anglesey, where it was formerly abundant, is called Puffin Island. Its original Anglo-Saxon name was *lunde*, which survives in Lundy (*Lunde-ey*, the Isle of Puffins), but has disappeared from common use. The bird has a number of vernacular names, affectionately given, including Sea Parrot, Bottlenose, Tommie Noddie, Tammy Nory and Coulterneb (*coulter*, the iron blade fixed in front of the share in a plough, and *neb*, a bill or nose). Its Linnæan name is not *Puffinus*, as logically it should be, but *Fratercula* (little brother), which is eminently more attractive.

Field Characteristics

THE following section gives, briefly, the field characters of the sea birds breeding in the British Isles, together with short references to the winter visitors and commoner vagrants. For convenience the birds are grouped under their natural orders and placed in approximately the same sequence as in the *Handbook of British Birds*. In certain of these species the sexes differ slightly in size, but there are no plumage differences and the colouring of the soft parts appears to be the same. In the field behaviour is the only criterion by which they can be distinguished.

Order PELECANIFORMES. This order contains five families of fish-eating birds. Two, the cormorants (*Phalacrocoracidae*) and the gannets (*Sulidae*), are represented in the British Isles. The families differ considerably in their appearance, but all have the hallux turned forwards and all four digits connected by webs.

The cormorants (pp. 16-32) have long necks, fairly long wings, wedge-shaped tails and short legs placed far back towards the base of the tail. Their bills are cylindrical, with a sharp hook at the end of the upper mandible. Two species, the Common Cormorant and the Shag, breed in the British Isles. In both the adults are largely blackish in colour and the juvenile birds dark brown. They are essentially coastal birds and are seldom seen far from land. Most individuals remain with us throughout the year. The **Common Cormorant**, *Phalacrocorax c. carbo* can be distinguished from the Shag at all times by its larger size and the presence of a white patch on the throat and cheeks. In the adult the body feathers have a bluish sheen. In the nuptial season it also has a characteristic white area on the flanks which is very conspicuous when it is flying. Immature birds are usually markedly paler or even whitish on the breast and belly. In addition to sea coasts this species often occurs in estuaries, and may visit neighbouring areas of fresh

The Common Cormorant

water. In parts of Ireland and Scotland it is found on lochs and rivers at some distance from the sea. The approximate areas within which it breeds regularly are shown by blacking in of the sea on the accompanying map: areas of sporadic breeding are stippled. Nesting birds may be seen at a number of places; two good sites are Puffin Island off Anglesey and Little Harcar in the Farne Islands. A second sub-species, the **Southern Cormorant**, *P. carbo sinensis*, inhabits the adjacent portions of the Continent and has been recorded several times on the English coast between Dorset and Suffolk. In breeding plumage it can be distinguished by a much greater development of the white feathers on the neck and head, so that the crown, nape and a collar round the neck are white or whitish. Juveniles and birds in winter plumage cannot be separated from

The Shag

the Common Cormorant in the field. The **Shag**, *P. a. aristotelis*, is markedly smaller than the Common Cormorant, with a more slender bill, no white feathering and a conspicuous area of yellow skin at the gape. The adults have a decided greenish sheen at all times and, in the nuptial season, a forward-jutting crest, like the unbrushed hair of a schoolboy. In immature birds the underparts are usually darker than in the young Common Cormorant, with whitish areas on the throat and round the vent. In general the Shag is restricted to the rockier coasts, and it does not normally frequent fresh water. It is less plentiful than the Common Cormorant in the south, but much more numerous in the north. The approximate areas within which it breeds regularly are shown by blacking in of the sea on the accompanying map. There is an easily accessible colony on Staple Island in the Farne Islands.

The gannets are large birds with fairly short necks, long, well-shaped wings and long, wedge-shaped tails. Their bills are stout and pointed. Only one species, the **Northern Gannet**, *Sula bassana*, occurs in British waters. It is essentially a maritime bird, frequenting off-shore waters, and in the winter months is often encountered in the open sea. It breeds in compact colonies on small, isolated islands at which some birds at least are present from February to September. Its form and habits are highly characteristic and sufficient to distinguish it from any other sea bird occurring in British waters. In the adult the plumage is white, rising to pale

123

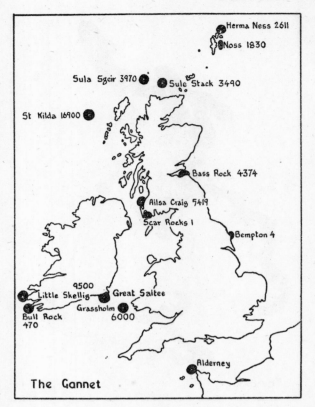

Herma Ness 2611
Noss 1830
Sula Sgeir 3970
Sule Stack 3490
St Kilda 16900
Bass Rock 4374
Ailsa Craig 5419
Scar Rocks 1
Bempton 4
9500
Little Skellig
Great Saltee
Grassholm
Bull Rock
470
6000
Alderney

The Gannet

straw yellow on the neck and head, with the primaries blackish brown. Juvenile birds are slate-black spotted with white above, and whitish with a greyish brown edging to the feathers underneath. The change to adult plumage is spread over three or four years. Twenty-three breeding-sites are at present known to be occupied, of which fourteen, marked on the accompanying map, are in the British Isles. The figures after the place-names give the approximate number of occupied nests as recorded in the census of 1939, except in the case of the colonies on Great Saltee and off Alderney, which were not active in that year. There were also formerly colonies on Copinsay in the Orkneys, the Stags of Broadhaven off County Mayo, and Lundy: a pair attempted to nest on the Isle of May in 1922, but the site has not been occupied since. C. E. Palmar tells me that the Scar Rocks colony has developed well with forty nests in 1945 and twenty-eight young birds in 1946. Great Saltee, like Bempton, has been slow in getting established and a few pairs have bred there at intervals since 1929. Nothing is known of the early history of the colony off Alderney: it was not in existence in 1940 and had about four hundred and fifty nests on three sites when R. M. Lockley visited it in June 1946. The most accessible breeding-ground is probably Ailsa Craig, which can be reached by boat from Girvan.

Order **PROCELLARIIFORMES.** This order contains a large number of essentially oceanic birds, coming to land only during the breeding season and feeding mostly on plankton or floating offal. They include the petrels, shearwaters and albatrosses. They vary considerably in size and form, but all have the nostrils enclosed in a pair of horny tubes placed, in the north Atlantic species, close together on the upper surface of the bill. Two families, the storm petrels (*Hydrobatidae*) and the shearwaters and fulmars (*Procellariidae*), are represented in the British Isles. They have no seasonal changes of plumage and the immature birds resemble the adults.

The storm petrels (pp. 38-40) are small, sooty brown birds with white rumps. Their typical habitat is the open sea and they are rarely seen in coastal waters except during the breeding season, though storm-driven birds occasionally arrive inland, even as far as the midlands, after spring and autumn gales. They nest on small, relatively isolated islands and are normally entirely nocturnal in their movements over the land. Two species, the Storm Petrel and Leach's Forktailed Petrel, breed in the British Isles. The **Storm Petrel**, *Hydrobates pelagicus*, can be distinguished by its small size, shorter wings, square-cut tail and an irregular whitish patch on the middle of the under surface of the wings. Its flight is weaker and more fluttering than that of the other species occurring in British waters. It breeds on the Scilly Isles, several islands off the coast of Wales and the north and west coasts of Ireland, many of the western isles of Scotland, the Orkneys and the Shetlands. The most accessible colony is on Skokholm, off the coast of Pembrokeshire. **Leach's Forktailed Petrel**, *Oceanodroma l. leucorrhoa*, is larger, with a wilder, freer flight and a distinctly forked tail. It has no white under the wings, and the white area on the rump, broad at the sides, is nearly interrupted in the midline. Its principal breeding-grounds in the Atlantic are off the coast of North America. Four colonies, marked on the accompanying map, are at present known to occur in the British Isles. It also formerly bred on islands off the coasts of Kerry and County Mayo in Ireland. Two nearly related species have occurred in British waters. The **Madeiran Forktailed Petrel**, *O. castro*, has its nearest breeding-grounds in the Azores, Madeira and the Salvages. It has been recorded from the south coast of England three times and the coast of Mayo once. It resembles Leach's Petrel, from which it can barely be distinguished in the field, except that the tail is less markedly forked and the white band on the rump is of even width all the way across. **Wilson's Petrel**, *Oceanites oceanicus*, which breeds in the Antarctic, spends the northern summer and early autumn in the north Atlantic up to the narrows between Newfoundland and Ireland, and has been reported from British waters on several occasions. It is midway in size between the Storm Petrel and Leach's Petrel, with a square-cut tail like the former. It can be distinguished by a paler band on the upper wing coverts, dark under wing coverts and much longer legs, with the feet, which have the webs yellow, projecting beyond the tail in flight. The Storm Petrel and Wilson's Petrel habitually follow ships: the Madeiran Petrel may do: Leach's Petrel never does.

The shearwaters are medium-sized sea birds, with rather elongated, slender bills, long, narrow wings and wedge-shaped tails. Like the storm petrels their true home is over the open sea, though certain of them keep to off-shore rather than mid-ocean waters. They come to land only to breed and move to and from their nesting-sites at night.

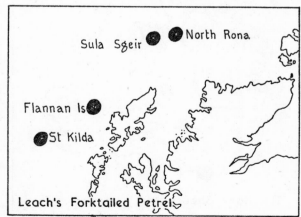

Leach's Forktailed Petrel

They are stronger on the wing than the storm petrels and are seldom carried inland by bad weather. The flight of the larger species is highly characteristic. It is a lovely movement of long, sweeping glides, very close to the water, broken by short periods of quick wing beats. They usually follow an erratic course, curving first to one side and then to the other, and frequently bank sharply with the lower wing almost touching the sea. One species, the Manx Shearwater, breeds in the British Isles, while several others occasionally stray into our coastal waters. The **Manx Shearwater**, *Puffinus p. puffinus*, is a rich, slightly brownish black above and white below, with a wing span of about thirty inches. When banking it shows the dorsal and ventral surfaces in sudden flashes of black and white. Its breeding range is fairly similar to that of the Storm Petrel, though colonies are less numerous and, on the whole, larger: the principal areas are marked by blacking in of the adjacent sea on the accompanying map, some of the minor ones by stippling. The most accessible sites are on some of the Welsh islands, particularly Skomer, Skokholm and Bardsey. A distinct sub-species, the **Balearic Shearwater**, *P. p. mauretanicus*, which breeds on a few islands in the western Mediterranean, has been recorded twenty-nine times on the English coast between Northumberland and Devon, mostly in August and September, and is said to occur in large numbers at the entry to the English Channel in October. It differs from the Manx Shearwater in having the upper parts much paler and the underparts tinged with sooty brown or greyish brown: on the wing it does not show the sudden, sharp contrasts between the dorsal and ventral surfaces. Another species, the **Madeiran Little Shearwater**, *P. assimilis baroli*, which breeds on Madeira, the Salvages and the Canary Isles, has been recorded eight times on the English coast between Norfolk and Sussex and once from Ireland. It resembles the Manx Shearwater in general colouring, but is much smaller and flaps its wings more frequently, seldom gliding for more than the briefest periods except in a strong wind. This bird is the nearest representative of a widely scattered group, now classified as two species with numerous sub-species, which breeds on a number of islands in the warmer parts of the Atlantic, Pacific and Indian Oceans. Most of them can-

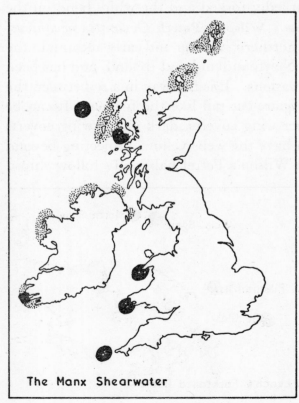

The Manx Shearwater

not be distinguished from each other with certainty in the field. Two other members, the **Cape Verde Little Shearwater**, *P. assimilis boydii*, and **Audubon's Shearwater**, *P. l. l'herminieri*, have also been recorded on the coast of Sussex, the former twice, in 1914 and 1915, and the latter once, in 1936. Three of the larger shearwaters, with wing spans ranging from thirty-six to forty-four inches, occasionally stray into British waters. One, the **Great Shearwater**, *P. gravis*, with a span of forty to forty-three inches, breeds on Tristan da Cunha and spends the northern summer and autumn in some numbers in the north Atlantic. It appears first off the American coast in May, and then moves up over the Newfoundland Bank to Greenland waters, returning south, from August to November, nearer the western approaches to the British Isles. It has been recorded from British waters, mostly on the west side, on a number of occasions. It is brown above, like the Balearic Shearwater, but with the wings and tail darker, a white patch on the rump and the top of the head almost black. The underparts are white, with dark flecks on the belly, and the white throat carried back so that it almost completely encircles the neck. Its characteristic feature is the sharp line between the brown of the head and the white of the neck and throat, which makes the former stand out like a dark skull cap. The **North Atlantic Shearwater**, *P. kuhlii borealis* (formerly known as **Cory's Shearwater**), is about the same size and colouring, except that the under surface is pure white, the patch on the rump less marked and the head and hind neck greyish brown: the bill is yellowish horn. Its distinguishing feature in flight is the absence of the dark cap on the head and the pure white belly. Its nearest breeding-grounds are off the coast of Portugal, Madeira and the Azores. At the end of the nesting season it disperses north and west, reaching European and American waters in some numbers up to about forty-eight degrees to fifty degrees north latitude: in November it withdraws to areas south of its breeding-grounds. It has only been taken twice on the English coast (Kent, 1901, and Sussex, 1914), but it would seem to be fairly plentiful off the western approaches to the English Channel in the autumn and has been seen at sea on a number of occasions. The typical race of this species, the **Mediterranean Shearwater**, *P. k. kuhlii*, breeds on a number of islands in the Mediterranean. It occurs much less frequently in the north Atlantic, but has been taken once on the coast of Sussex. It cannot be distinguished from the foregoing in the field. The **Sooty Shearwater**, *P. griseus*, is slightly smaller, with a wing span of thirty-six to forty inches, and much more uniform in colouring. It is blackish brown above and greyish brown beneath, with the under wing coverts greyish white. Its nearest breeding-grounds are off Cape Horn and in the Falkland Isles. Outside the breeding season it ranges over the north Atlantic, like the Great Shearwater, but it is scarcer and seldom extends beyond the narrows between Ireland and Newfoundland. It is an occasional autumn visitor to British waters, occurring equally on both coasts.

The **Fulmar**, *Fulmarus g. glacialis*, is the only example of the bulkier petrels

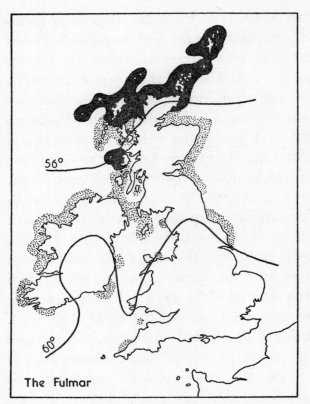

56°

60°

The Fulmar

that occurs in British waters. Unlike the shearwater it nests on exposed sites, instead of in burrows, and comes to land by day. It follows ships and scavenges freely. In general colouring it resembles the gulls, but can be distinguished by its heavy, tubular bill and, in the air, by its characteristic flight, gliding and banking frequently with its long, narrow wings fully extended and rigid. At the present time it is plentiful off our northern coasts from December to September and may be seen at suitable points farther south. The main breeding areas are shown by blacking in of the adjacent sea on the accompanying map, the minor ones by stippling.

Order CHARADRIIFORMES, Sub-order LARI. This sub-order contains two families, the gulls and terns (*Laridae*) and the skuas (*Stercorariidae*), which are both well represented in the British Isles.

The terns are small to medium-sized sea birds with long, tapering wings, fairly long, tapering bills, short legs and small feet. The majority, including all those normally occurring in Britain, have long, deeply forked tails. Five species nest here regularly and a sixth formerly bred in England: five others have been recorded as rare vagrants. The breeding species (pp. 61-66) are essentially coastal birds and are seldom seen far from land except when migrating. They rarely alight on the water, but frequently rest on rocks, posts or the shore itself, standing with the body parallel with the ground and the head sunk down so that the nape is in line with the back. Their flight is light and buoyant, with the wing beats, each of which raises them perceptibly, deliberate and rather slow. They feed mostly on small fish. They usually take their food from the surface of the sea, plunging from a height of ten to twenty feet or, occasionally, swooping down and picking it up without entering the water. They never scavenge and do not follow boats. Their calls are usually harsh and raucous. The summer plumage differs slightly from the winter plumage. The latter is generally developed in July or August, but in some cases the moult may begin earlier. The nuptial plumage is usually acquired between February and April. As they arrive in Britain in May and leave for the winter between July and September, both patterns are seen on our coasts. All five species are very similar in colouring and some are difficult to distinguish from each other in the field. In general they are white, with the mantle and dorsal surface of the wings pale grey and the primaries marked with dark slate-grey; some also have a varying amount of light grey on the tail. In summer the top of the head and nape are jet black, and in some species the breast and belly may have a faint pinkish blush. Juvenile birds differ from the adults in having the crown, mantle and wing coverts mottled. The **Sandwich Tern**, *Sterna s. sandvicensis*, is larger and heavier than the other species; its bill is black with a yellow tip, and its legs and feet black. In summer it can also be distinguished by the elongation of the feathers of the nape which blow untidily in the wind like the proverbial artist's

The Sandwich Tern

uncut hair. In winter plumage the forehead is white and the crown and nape white with black streaks: the autumn moult begins on the head and may start as early as June or even the end of May. Juvenile birds have the forehead ash-brown, the crown streaked with white and brownish black, the tail slate-grey and the remaining upper parts mottled with black and white. This bird occurs as a passage migrant in spring and autumn, principally on the south and east coasts. It breeds in colonies of varying size at a number of points: the principal areas are marked approximately by blacking in of the sea on the accompanying map, and some of the subsidiary ones by stippling. Colonies fluctuate greatly in size from year to year and the sites are often changed. The best of the more accessible spots are Ravenglass, the Farne Islands and near Scolt Head in Norfolk: in 1946 there was a fine colony on the Isle of May, though the birds had not previously bred there in large numbers. The **Little Tern**, *S. a. albifrons*, is the smallest of the British species; its bill is yellow with a black tip and the legs and feet orange-yellow. In summer it can also be distinguished by its white forehead. In winter the lores are also white and the crown is mottled: the nape remains black. Juvenile birds differ in having the crown buffy white streaked with black, and the upper parts grey mottled with sandy buff. The Little Tern occurs as a migrant on many parts of the coast and occasionally inland. It breeds in small colonies on sand or shingle beaches at a number of scattered points, mostly within the areas marked by stippling on the map on page 130. The

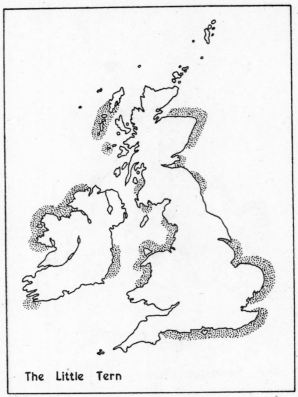

The Little Tern

remaining three species are very similar in size and colouring. The **Common Tern**, *S. h. hirundo*, has the bill coral-red with a black tip and the legs and feet red in summer. In winter the soft parts are mostly black, and the forehead and lores white. Juvenile birds also have the mantle mottled with ash-brown, an ash-grey band on the upper wing coverts and the outer webs of the tail feathers dark brown. The Common Tern occurs as a passage migrant and breeding bird at a number of points all round the British coast, except in south Wales; in Scotland and Ireland it also nests on inland lochs and some rivers. In western Ireland, north-west Scotland, the Orkneys and the Shetlands it is much less plentiful than the Arctic Tern, and in the last two areas it is scarce. The **Arctic Tern**, *S. macrura*, is very similar to the Common Tern except that in the summer the bill is usually entirely blood-red, and in the juvenile yellow with a black tip instead of brownish. These points are not easy to see in the field, and diagnosis often depends on the fact that it is markedly shorter in the leg, with the tail streamers usually relatively longer and the wings shorter. The alarm notes are also slightly different; the Arctic Tern when annoyed frequently emits a harsh *kee-yaah*, with the accent on the second syllable, in place of the Common Tern's rather higher-pitched *peeee-yah*. It also has a rather characteristic rising squeak, *kee-kee-kee*, when excited. The Arctic Tern occurs as a passage migrant on all coasts. It is rare as a breeding bird in England and, except for a few pairs in Norfolk, Anglesey and a recently re-established colony in the Scilly Isles, usually does not occur south of the Farne Islands in the east and the Isle of Man in the west. In Scotland it is plentiful, particularly towards the north, while in the Orkneys and Shetlands it is usually the only tern seen. Areas in which it is plentiful or the predominant species are shown by blacking in of the adjacent sea on the accompanying map : additional areas within which it may occur are stippled. The **Roseate Tern**, *S. d. dougallii*, is also fairly similar in colouring except that in summer it has the bill black, dropping to vermilion at its base, and frequently a marked rose blush on the breast and belly; unfortunately the latter is more obvious in print than in the field. The outer tail feathers are white and much longer than in the

The Arctic Tern

The Roseate Tern

other terns: this latter point is equally noticeable in the air and on the ground. In general it also appears whiter in colour and much more slender in form than the other species. Its usual note when alarmed or quarrelling is a loud, harsh *kaaak*. It occurs only as a summer visitor or an occasional vagrant. It breeds in small units at a limited number of points, mostly within the areas marked by blacking in of the adjacent sea on the accompanying map, among colonies of other terns. If possible it places its eggs in a hollow among boulders, or close to outcrops of rock. Two of the rare vagrants have somewhat similar colouring to the preceding species. The **Caspian Tern**, *Hydropogne caspia*, which has been recorded about thirty times, mostly on the coast from Northumberland to Dorset, is much larger than the Sandwich Tern and is distinguished from it by its stout, deep red bill. The **Gull-billed Tern**, *Gelochelidon n. nilotica*, which has occurred about forty times, mostly in England, is a little smaller than the Sandwich Tern, with a short, stout, completely black bill and a less deeply forked tail. The remaining terns are smaller and mainly dark in plumage. Three of these are marsh terns, breeding on lakes and swamps in western or southern Europe. They are most likely to be seen over fresh water. The **Black Tern**, *Chlidonias n. niger*, which formerly bred in England, still occurs fairly frequently as a passage migrant, mostly between Kent and Norfolk; in Ireland and southern Scotland it is an occasional vagrant. In summer plumage it is dark lead-grey, rising to black on the head, paler on the wings and tail, with the under wing coverts light grey and the under tail coverts white. In winter it is white, with the crown and nape mottled with dark grey, and the mantle, wings and tail slate-grey. The **Whitewinged Black Tern**, *C. leucopterus*, which has occurred several times in England, Wales and Ireland, is rather similar, except that the tail and lesser wing coverts are white and, in summer, the underwing black. The **Whiskered Tern**, *C. h. hybrida*, which has been recorded on about twenty-two occasions, is largely slate-grey in summer with the throat, lores and cheeks white and the top of the head black: the bill is blood-red. In winter the underparts are white and the crown streaked with white. The **Sooty Tern**, *S. f. fuscata*, which is essentially pelagic rather than coastal, is brownish black above and white below, with a broad white band on the forehead ending above the eyes. Its nearest breeding-grounds are off the southern coast of the United States, the West Indies, Ascension and St. Helena. It has been recorded about fifteen times in southern Britain.

The gulls are medium to fairly large-sized sea birds, with long wings, almost square-cut tails and shortish legs. They have stout, wedge-shaped bills, with the upper mandible hooked at its tip and the lower angulated on its lower edge. Six species breed in the British Isles (pp. 67-92), and a further eight occur as winter visitors or occasional vagrants. Their food is varied, but, with one exception, all scavenge freely when they have the opportunity to do so. Their flight is powerful and buoyant. They glide frequently and with consummate ease. Normally the wings are not fully extended, but are held with the joints slightly flexed so that the angle of the wrist is clearly apparent. This point differentiates them from the Fulmar which, like the albatrosses, flies with the wings rigid and fully spread. In general adult gulls are mainly white in the summer, with the mantle and wings grey or blackish. In winter the head is frequently mottled with a varying number of greyish or brownish feathers. The winter plumage is acquired by a complete moult, usually taking place between July and November, the summer by a partial moult between January and April. The juveniles are usually mottled with varying shades of blackish or greyish brown on a light brown ground. The full adult plumage is often not reached until the third,

The Common Gull

fourth or even fifth year, depending on the size of the species, and the change is usually a gradual one. The **Herring Gull**, *Larus a. argentatus*, is the best introduction to the British gulls. It is fairly large, with a span of about fifty inches. The adult plumage is white, with the mantle and greater part of the wings pale blue-grey. The wing has a narrow white border along its hind edge and a triangular brownish black tip, marked with white spots or mirrors. The bill is deep yellow, with a bright vermilion mark on the gonys, and the legs and feet flesh coloured. The juvenile plumage is light umber-brown, mottled with dark, blackish brown. It is essentially a coastal bird and a determined and persistent scavenger. In winter it is plentiful all round the British Isles and may occur inland; it is slightly less numerous in the north. Its breeding range is almost equally extensive. Except for the stretch between the Humber and the Thames there is no coastal county in which it does not nest, though it is less common in the more populated areas. A sub-species, the **Scandinavian Herring Gull**, *L. a. omissus*, inhabits northern Europe and individuals have been taken in England on several occasions. It differs in having the mantle darker than in the British race, but this is scarcely detectable in the field. Birds from the eastern portion of its range have distinctive yellow legs and feet, but unfortunately in those from Scandinavia they are flesh coloured. The **Common Gull**, *L. c. canus*, resembles the Herring Gull,

The Lesser Blackbacked Gull

The Great Blackbacked Gull

The Kittiwake

The Blackheaded Gull

but is smaller with a relatively more slender bill. In the adult it can be distinguished, apart from its size and more refined appearance, by the colour of its bill, legs and feet, which are a uniform greenish yellow. Juvenile birds are whitish on the forehead, throat and base of the tail, and paler on the remainder of the under surface. The Common Gull is plentiful in England as a winter visitor, but rarely seen in summer. The principal coastal breeding areas are shown approximately by blacking in of the adjacent sea on the map on page 132; minor areas by stippling. The **British Lesser Blackbacked Gull**, *L. fuscus graellsii*, is a little smaller than the Herring Gull. The essential characteristics of the adult are its dark slate-grey back and wings, and bright yellow legs and feet. Juvenile birds in their first year cannot be distinguished from young Herring Gulls. Later the wings and mantle become darker. It is fairly widely distributed on all coasts throughout the year, and in parts occurs inland. The principal coastal breeding areas are marked by blacking in of the adjacent sea on the map on page 133; some of the occasional sites are stippled. The typical race of this bird, the **Scandinavian Lesser Blackbacked Gull**, *L. f. fuscus*, occurs in north Europe and occasionally reaches Britain as a passage migrant or winter visitor. It differs in having the mantle in the adult slate-black, like the next species; in British birds the body of the wing is noticeably paler than the tips of the primaries, while in the Scandinavian ones it is

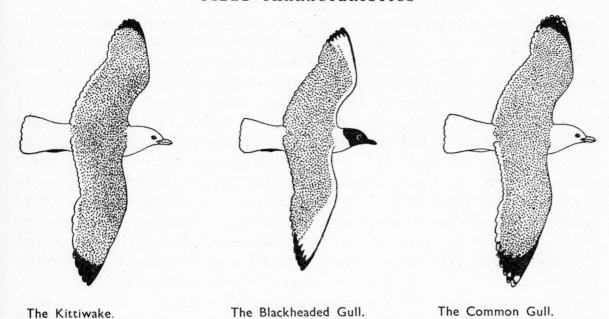

The Kittiwake.   The Blackheaded Gull.   The Common Gull.

Adult birds in summer plumage.   Wing patterns are the same in winter plumage.

the same colour. The **Great Blackbacked Gull**, *L. marinus*, is appreciably larger. The adult has the mantle and wings almost black, and the feet flesh coloured. It also has a more arrogant poise, which is at times most conspicuous. Juvenile birds have a much lighter ground colour than those of the Herring and Lesser Blackbacked Gulls, with the markings relatively smaller and more clearly defined. It is less plentiful than the preceding species, but equally widely distributed, winter visitors, and in summer non-breeding birds, occurring on all coasts. It is seldom seen inland. It is easily the most numerous species on the Yarmouth fishing-grounds in autumn. The principal breeding areas are marked on the map on page 133 by blacking in of the adjacent sea, some of the minor sites by stippling. The **Kittiwake**, *Rissa t. tridactyla*, is about the same size as the Common Gull. The adult is fairly similar in colouring, but differs in having no white mirrors on the primaries, the mantle darker rather than paler than the wings, and the legs and feet brownish black. Its characteristic call, *kitti-waake, kitti-waake*, is highly distinctive. Juvenile birds resemble the adult except for some blackish mottling over the eye and round the ear, a broad black collar on the hind neck and a black terminal band on the tail: the back is also mottled with black and there is a diagonal blackish bar across the wing to the wrist which is continued along the outer primaries. The Kittiwake is more maritime than the other gulls and disappears over the open sea outside the breeding season, spreading across the north Atlantic from sixty degrees north latitude to the tropic of Cancer. It never scavenges on the land and is never found round estuaries and harbours. It breeds in large numbers on suitable, precipitous cliffs, principally within the areas shown approximately on the map on page 134 by blacking in of the adjacent sea: some minor sites are marked by stippling. The **Blackheaded Gull**, *L. r. ridibundus*, is smaller and slighter in build than the Kittiwake, with a deep red, more slender bill. In the adult the wing is markedly different, being a fairly uniform blue-grey, except for a band along the front edge, broadening to include the greater part of the outer five primaries, which is white. The inner margin and tips of the outer primaries are an unbroken black, with no white spots or mirrors. In the nuptial season adults have a coffee-brown hood, which is reduced in winter to a few dusky markings in the neighbourhood of the eye and ear. Juvenile birds differ from the adults in having the mantle an uneven brown, with some brownish grey on the wing coverts and the back of the head, and a subterminal blackish brown band on the tail. The principal breeding areas, which are frequently inland, are shown approximately by blacking on the map on page 134: minor sites are stippled. Outside the breeding season it spreads widely and occurs on a number of lakes, reservoirs and semi-tidal rivers, away from its nesting-grounds, as well as on estuaries, harbours and low-lying, sheltered coasts. A closely related species, the **Mediterranean Blackheaded Gull**, *L. melanocephalus*, occurs in south-eastern Europe and Asia Minor, and has been recorded on about ten occasions from south-eastern England. It has a much stouter bill than the British bird with, in the adult, no black on the ends of the primaries: in the breeding season the hood is black instead of dark brown and the white round the eye reduced to thin bars above and below the orbit. Juvenile birds differ in having a brown not white band along the forward edge of the wing. The **Little Gull**, *L. minutus*, which occurs as an occasional winter visitor on the east coast of England and, more rarely, Scotland and Ireland, is somewhat similar to the British Blackheaded Gull, but it is much smaller. It also has no black on the tips of its primaries. The under surface of the wing is greyish black instead of pale blue-grey. In breeding birds the hood is jet black, with no pale ring round the eye. The nearest regular breeding-grounds are in the Baltic, but in 1942 fifteen pairs nested in northern Holland. **Sabine's Gull**, *Xema sabini*, which is slightly larger, also occurs on the eastern coasts of England, Scotland and Ireland as an occasional autumn and winter visitor. It has a markedly forked tail, distinguishing it from all other gulls in British waters, and a short, stout bill. In the adult the wing has most of the primary region up to the wrist black, with a conspicuous white triangle in the region of the secondaries. In breeding plumage the hood is dark grey, with a black border where it joins the white of the neck. Three further species, much lighter in their general colouring, occur as occasional or regular winter visitors, especially in the north. The largest of these, the **Glaucous Gull** (or **Burgomaster**), *L. hyperboreus*, usually arrives in small numbers, but in a severe winter it may be very plentiful along the east coast from Norfolk to the Shetlands, and fairly numerous in northern Ireland, the Hebrides

| Longtailed Skua | Pomatorhine Skua | Arctic Skua |

Adults of the longtailed skuas in flight. All three are shown in the light phase: in the dark phase the heads and bodies appear a uniform off-black when the birds are in flight, but the diagnostic features, size, the shape of the tail and wing bar (here shown slightly exaggerated) remain unchanged.

and north Scotland. It is about the size of the Greater Blackbacked Gull, which it dominates when the two meet, with a coarse, heavy bill. The adult has the mantle and wings a uniform light grey, paler than the Herring Gull, with no black on the primaries. In winter plumage the head and underparts are lightly streaked with pale brown. Juveniles are a creamish or whitish buff, mottled with pale brown, with the primaries brown. The **Iceland Gull**, *L. glaucoides*, occurs more irregularly and in much smaller numbers. It resembles the Glaucous Gull at all stages, but is smaller, with a more slender bill and relatively longer wings. In the adult the orbital ring is pinkish brown or dull brick-red, not yellow as in the Glaucous Gull. The **Ivory Gull**, *Pagophila eburnea*, is the rarest of the three, and has only been recorded about seventy times, mostly from the Shetlands and Orkneys. It is about the size of the Common Gull. The adult is pure white, with a bright yellow bill and black legs and feet: the juvenile is white with blackish mottling on the head, back and wings, and a narrow, black terminal band on the tail.

The skuas (pp. 93-97) are moderately large birds, with powerful, thick-set bodies, long, well-developed wings and short, stout legs. Their beaks are stout and hooked. They resemble the scavenging gulls in many ways, but are darker in colouring and more predatory in their habits. They are also more essentially maritime and outside the breeding season disperse to off-shore waters or the open sea. Two species, the Great Skua and the Arctic or Richardson's Skua, breed in the northern parts of the British Isles: two others occur on our coasts as passage migrants, chiefly in the autumn. The most accessible places covering both the resident birds are the sanctuaries on Herma Ness and Noss in the Shetlands, and Hoy in the Orkneys. The **Great Skua**, *Stercorarius s. skua*, is larger than the other species and appreciably more bulky in appearance. It has a short, almost square-cut tail. In general colouring it is a dusky, dark greyish brown, streaked with yellowish brown on the neck and back, and tinged with rufous-brown on the underparts. The basal portions of the inner webs of the primaries are white, forming a conspicuous white triangular patch when the wings are extended. The juvenile plumage is fairly similar to that of the adult, but darker and duller. The normal flight of the Great Skua is rather like that of a gull, but it appears much heavier in the air and its movements more laboured. When swooping it comes down in a steep glide, often with the wings at an angle of about forty-five degrees, but it never falls through the air as the gulls do. The Great Skua is seldom seen except at its breeding-grounds, though it may occur as an occasional winter visitor, especially on the east coast. It breeds at several points in the Shetlands (particularly north-west Unst, Yell, Fetlar, Hascosay, Bressay, Noss, Mousa and Foula), Fair Isle and Hoy. The other skuas are slightly smaller, with more slender heads and bodies and, in the adult, a marked elongation of the central pair of tail feathers. They are very agile in the air and, when necessary, can move extremely fast. The **Arctic Skua**, *S. parasiticus*, has two colour phases; the darker birds are a uniform dark ash-brown above and slightly paler, sooty brown beneath; paler birds have the sides of the head and neck straw-yellow, and the chin and breast dull white. The proportion of the two phases varies considerably at the different breeding-grounds, dark birds ranging from less than one to ninety-five per cent. The important characteristic is the shape of the tail, which is long and cuneiform, with the central two feathers elongated and pointed. Juvenile birds of the darker phase are a sooty, greyish brown, barred with buff on the rump, flanks, breast and belly: lighter birds have the upper surface dark greyish brown, spotted with buff on the back, and the head and underparts dull buff, barred with sooty grey. The central tail feathers are pointed but not elongated. The Arctic Skua breeds in the Shetlands, Fair Isle, Orkneys, Inner and Outer Hebrides, Caithness and, a few scattered pairs, in Sutherland. It occurs fairly frequently elsewhere on the British coasts as a passage migrant, mostly in the autumn and chiefly on the east and south sides. The **Pomatorhine Skua**, *S. pomarinus*, which breeds mostly on the tundras north of the Arctic circle and winters in the southern tropics, also occurs in Britain as an autumn passage migrant and occasionally as a winter visitor. It is seen most frequently on the east and south coasts of England. It is larger than the Arctic Skua, with the same two colour phases: dark birds are relatively less numerous and represent less than ten per cent of the total. Its distinctive characteristic in the adult is the peculiar formation of the central tail feathers, which are much elongated, broad, blunt-ended and twisted, so that they are equally conspicuous from the side and from beneath. The adults also have a light band on the wing, like that of the Great Skua, but smaller and less marked. The **Longtailed Skua**, *S. longicaudus*, is smaller and slighter than the Arctic Skua. Melanic forms are rare and in most areas only the pale phase occurs. Adults can be recognized by the extreme elongation of the central tail feathers and the slightly more greyish colouring of the upper parts. Juvenile birds cannot be distinguished with certainty in the field. This bird is comparatively scarce in British waters, but it occurs occasionally as a passage migrant, mostly in the autumn and on the east coast of England.

Order CHARADRIIFORMES, Sub-order ALCAE. This sub-order contains only one family, the auks (*Alcidae*), which is represented in the British Isles by four breeding species: two additional species occur as irregular winter vagrants. The auks are small, diving birds, essentially maritime in their habits, with short necks, rather squat bodies, very short tails and small, narrow wings. Their feet, which have only three toes, are large, webbed and placed far back, near the base of the tail, so that on land they habitually adopt an almost upright stance. Their flight is laboured, and usually of short duration: the wings are moved rapidly through a short arc so that they seem to vibrate rather than beat. They swim and dive well, feeding below the surface. They usually nest in large, compact colonies and outside the breeding season spend their time at sea in off-shore or open waters. Bad weather may drive them on to lee shores; otherwise they are seldom seen in the winter months.

Little Auk — winter adult.

Black Guillemot — winter adult.

Black Guillemot — juvenile.

Common Guillemot — winter adult.

Many of the breeding-grounds are relatively inaccessible, though the birds can often be watched from a distance. The most accessible sites, where all except the Black Guillemot occur in large numbers, are probably Lundy and Skomer. Common Guillemots and Puffins are also plentiful on the Farne Islands. All four species can

The Black Guillemot

The Puffin

be seen on a number of the northern islands, of which Handa, off the coast of Sutherland, and Unst, in the Shetlands, are probably the best. Except for the Black Guillemot, the general colouring of the British auks in summer is black or dark brown on the head and upper parts, with the under surface white. In winter the throat and cheeks may also be white or whitish. Young birds in general resemble the winter plumage of the adult. The **British Razorbill**, *Alca torda britannica*, has a large, compressed bill, a white line across the forehead to the eye, pointed tail feathers, and a neat, plump appearance. It breeds on suitable cliffs all round the coast except between south Yorkshire and the Isle of Wight. It is usually less plentiful than the Common Guillemot, except in Ireland. It frequents off-shore waters during the winter, and is often storm-driven on to the coast and may even occur inland. The **Common Guillemot**, *Uria aalge*, is slightly larger than the Razorbill and less shapely. It can be distinguished by its more slender bill and absence of the white line on the forehead. In adults in winter plumage and juvenile birds the white cheek is crossed by a thin black line running back from the eye. The Common Guillemots are divided into two races. The more northern sub-species, *U. a. aalge*, appear black above, like the Razorbill, though its head is slightly browner. The southern sub-species, *U. aalge albionis*, which occurs as far north as the Farne Islands and Ailsa Craig, is much paler and browner, but the two cannot always be distinguished with certainty in the field. The Common Guillemot has the same range in summer and winter as the Razorbill, but, except in Ireland, is much more plentiful. A northern species, **Brunnich's Guillemot**, *U. l. lomvia*, has strayed to the British coast about a dozen times. It has much the same colouring as the Northern Common Guillemot, but can be separated at close range by its shorter bill, with a white streak along the lower border of the upper mandible, and, in winter, by the absence of the black line on the cheeks. The **Black Guillemot**, *U. g. grylle*, is smaller and fatter than the Common Guillemot. In summer it appears largely black, with a distinctive white patch on both surfaces of the wing. In winter it is white, with the upper parts mottled with black and the wings and tail as in summer plumage. Juvenile birds resemble the adult in winter, except that the underparts and the white patch on the wings are also mottled with black. The Black Guillemot is much less plentiful than the Common Guillemot; it breeds sparsely in the area blacked in on the accompanying map, and sporadically within the stippled portions. British birds do not move south to any great extent during the winter, and it is rarely seen outside its breeding range. The **Little Auk**, *Alle a. alle*, which breeds north of the Arctic circle, occasionally occurs in British waters as a winter visitor. I once knew of a man who much wanted to see this bird and hired a boat to go to Spitzbergen to do so: when he returned he learnt that the autumn gales had driven two inland to Cambridge while he was on his way back. The Little Auk is a neat, compact, stumpy bird, about half the size of the Razorbill, with a short, almost sparrow-like, bill. In summer the head, neck and upper parts are glossy black, and the remainder of the underparts white. In winter adults and young birds the white spreads to include the chin, throat and region of the ears. The **Puffin**, *Fratercula arctica grabae*, is smaller and tubbier than the Razorbill. The adult can always be identified by its bright, triangular bill and grey face. Juvenile birds, which are smaller, with a much smaller bill, might be taken for Little Auks, but they are duller in colouring and less compact in shape. The Puffin is seldom seen during the winter months. In summer it breeds in dense colonies on suitable sites, mainly on islands, within the areas marked by blacking in of the sea on the accompanying map: a few birds nest within the stippled sections.

The following sea birds also occur on the British check list, but they have not been regarded as of sufficient importance to be included in the previous section of this book.

The **Frigate Petrel,** *Pelagodroma marina hypoleuca.* Recorded twice, Walney Island, Lancashire, in 1890, and Colonsay, Hebrides, in 1897. Distinguished by entirely white under surface and white streak over the eyes. Nearest breeding-grounds, Salvage, Canary and Cape Verde Islands.

The **Kermadec Petrel,** *Pterodroma neglecta.* Recorded once, Cheshire in 1908. Size of Manx Shearwater, colouring variable; distinguished by distinct white area towards the tip of the under surface of the wings. Breeds in the sub-tropical zone of the south Pacific.

The **Capped Petrel,** *Pterodroma hasitata.* Recorded once, Norfolk in 1850. Resembles the Great Shearwater, but has distinctly white nape and marked white area on the upper tail coverts. Formerly bred extensively in the West Indies: now probably occurs only on Dominica and Hispaniola.

The **Collared Petrel,** *Pterodroma leucoptera brevipes.* Recorded once, Cardigan in 1889. Smaller than the Manx Shearwater; dark above, with a grey area extending across the back and wings. Breeds in the Pacific on the New Hebrides and Fiji.

Bulwer's Petrel, *Bulweria bulwerii.* Recorded seven times, in Yorkshire and Sussex, between 1837 and 1914. Much smaller than the Manx Shearwater, with the plumage entirely sooty black. Nearest breeding-grounds, Madeira, Azores, Salvage and Canary Islands.

The **Blackbrowed Albatross,** *Diomedea melanophrys.* Taken once in Cambridgeshire in 1897: others seen in 1894 and 1895. From 1860 to 1894 (when it was shot by an ardent collector) an individual lived on the Faroes, associating with the Gannets and moving south with them each autumn. Nearest breeding-grounds in the Cape Horn area and on South Georgia: plentiful in the South Atlantic from 30° s. to 60° s.

The **Bridled Tern,** *Sterna a. anaethetus.* Recorded once, Kent in 1931. Resembles the Sooty Tern, but smaller, with the white band on the forehead narrower and extending back over the eyes. Probably breeds on islands off the west coast of Africa: an allied race occurs in the West Indies.

Ross's Gull, *Rhodostethia rosea.* Recorded once, Yorkshire in 1846 or 1847. About the size of the Little Gull, with the head and underparts rosy white and, in summer, a narrow black ring round the neck. Breeds in north-east Siberia and probably Greenland.

Bonaparte's Gull, *Larus philadelphia.* Recorded seven times, Belfast, Dumbarton, Cornwall and Sussex, between 1848 and 1913. Resembles the Blackheaded Gull, but smaller, with bill black and, in summer, hood dark slate-grey. Nearest breeding-grounds, northern Canada.

The **Great Blackheaded Gull,** *Larus ichthyaetus.* Taken twice, Devon in 1859 and Kent in 1915: others reported seen. Size of Great Blackbacked Gull: distinguished by heavy, orange bill, with blackish sub-terminal band, and greenish legs: hood, in summer, black. Nearest breeding-grounds, southern Russia.

The **Northern Razorbill,** *Alca t. torda.* Taken once, Kent in 1937. Not distinguishable from the British race in the field. Nearest breeding-grounds, from Heligoland along the coast of Norway to Iceland.

The **Great Auk,** *Alca impennis.* Extinct about 1844. Known to have bred on St. Kilda; probably also bred in the Orkneys. Extra-limital range included the Faroes, Iceland, Newfoundland and possibly Greenland.

A full bibliography is not possible in a work of this size and scope, but the following books and articles, the majority of which have been quoted or referred to in the text, are given as likely to be of particular interest to readers of this book.

General

ALEXANDER, W. B. *Birds of the Ocean.* (Putnams, 1928.)

DARLING, F. FRASER. *Bird Flocks and the Breeding Cycle.* (C.U.P., 1938.)
   Island Years. (Bell, 1940.)

DEWAR, J. M. *The Bird as a Diver.* (Witherby, 1924.)

WITHERBY, H. F., and others. *The Handbook of British Birds.* 5 vols. (Witherby, 1938-41. Reprinted with revisions, 1943.)

Pelecaniformes

FISHER, J., and VEVERS, H. G. "The North Atlantic Gannet." (*Journal of Animal Ecology*, Vol. XII, pp. 173-213, 1943, and Vol. XIII, pp. 49-62, 1944.)

GURNEY, J. H. *The Gannet.* (Witherby, 1913.)

KORTLANDT, A. "Levensloop, samenstellung en structuur der Nederlandse aalscholverbevolking." (*Ardea*, Vol. XXXI, pp. 175-280, 1942.)

LUMSDEN, W. H. R., and HADDOW, A. J. "The Food of the Shag in the Clyde Area." (*Journal of Animal Ecology*, Vol. XV, pp. 35-42, 1946.)

Procellariiformes

AINSLIE, J. A., and ATKINSON, R. "On the Breeding Habits of Leach's Forktailed Petrel." (*British Birds*, Vol. XXX, pp. 234-48 and 276-77, 1937.)

FISHER, J., and WATERSTON, G. "The Breeding Distribution of the Fulmar in the British Isles." (*Journal of Animal Ecology*, Vol. X, pp. 204-72, 1941.)

GROSS, W. A. O. "The Life Cycle of Leach's Petrel." (*Auk*, Vol. III, pp. 382-99, 1935.)

LOCKLEY, R. M. *Shearwaters.* (Dent, 1942.)

Charadriiformes

AUSTIN, O. L. "The role of longevity in successful breeding by the Common Tern." (*Bird Banding*, Vol. XVI, pp. 21-28, 1945.)

HOLLOM, P. A. D. "Report on the 1938 survey of Blackheaded Gull colonies." *British Birds*, Vol. XXXIII, pp. 202-21 and 230-44, 1940.)

KIRKMAN, T. B. *Bird Behaviour.* (Nelson, 1937.)

LOCKLEY, R. M. "On the breeding habits of the Puffin." (*British Birds*, Vol. XXVI, pp. 214-23, 1934.)

MARPLES, G. and A. *Sea Terns.* (Country Life, 1934.)

PERRY, R. B. *Lundy, Isle of Puffins.* (Lindsay Drummond, 1940.)

POOR, H. H. "Plumage and soft part variations in the Herring Gull." (*Auk*, Vol. LXIII, pp. 135-51, 1946.)

Index

ENGLISH NAMES

Numbers in italics (shown against English names only) refer to photograph pages. References are not given where birds are merely quoted as examples to illustrate a general proposition.

SCIENTIFIC NAMES